KU-247-464

CONTENTS

LIST OF CONTRIBUTORS

Dr. Margaret Atherden   PLACE Research Centre, University College of Ripon & York St. John, Lord Mayor's Walk, York, YO31 7EX.

Mr. Colin Avison   Countryside Research Unit, Sheffield Hallam University, City Campus, Pond Street, Sheffield, S1 1WB

Dr. Morag Bell   Dept. of Geography, University of Loughborough, Loughborough, LE 11 3TU

Mr. Simon Bell   Forestry Authority, 231 Corstorphine Rd., Edinburgh, EH12 7AT

Ms Christine Butler   BKS Surveys Ltd., Coleraine, Northern Ireland, BT51 3HZ

Prof. Robin Butlin   School of Geography, University of Leeds, Leeds, LS2 9JT

Mr. Alan Boyle   BKS Surveys Ltd., Coleraine, Northern Ireland, BT51 3HZ

Dr. Lois Child   Dept. of Geography, University of Loughborough, Loughborough, LE11 3TU

Prof. Andrew Fleming   Department of Archaeology, University of Wales, Lampeter, Ceredigion, SA48 7ED

Dr. Tom Gledhill   1 Hylton Terrace, Rookhope, Bishop Auckland, DL13 2BB

Mr. Stephen Hartley   School of Biology, University of Leeds, Leeds, LS2 9JT

Prof. Brian Huntley   Environmental Research Centre, University of Durham, Dept. of Biological Sciences, South Rd., Durham, DH1 3LE

Mr. Melvyn Jones	4 Kirkstead Abbey Mews, Thorpe Hesley, Rotherham, S61 2UZ
Mrs. Jennifer Kaner	77 Stockton Lane, York, YO31 0JA
Dr. Keith Kirby	English Nature, Northminster House, Peterborough, PE1 1UA
Dr. Christopher Lavers	Dept. of Geography, University of Nottingham, Nottingham, NG7 2RD
Mr. Monty Loftus	BKS Surveys Lrd., Coleraine, Northern Ireland, BT51 3HZ
Mr. Philip Lyth	Farming & Wildlife Advisory Group, 13 South Parade, Northallerton, DL7 8SL
Mr. Geordie McMillan,	BKS Surveys Ltd., Coleraine, Northern Ireland, BT51 3HZ
Mr. Ian Panter	York Archaeological Wood Centre, 13 Ogleforth, York YO1 2JG
Mr. Andrew Parkinson	Farming & Wildlife Advisory Group, 13 South Parade, Northallerton, DL7 8SL
Dr. Oliver Rackham	Corpus Christi College, Cambridge, CB2 1RH
Dr. Ian Rotherham	Countryside Research Unit, Sheffield Hallam University, City Campus, Pond Street, Sheffield, S1 1WB
Dr. Michel Ribodeau	School of Biology, University of Leeds, Leeds, LS2 9JT
Mr. Jim Spriggs	York Archaeological Wood Centre, 13 Ogleforth, York YO1 2JG
Dr. Charles Watkins	Dept. of Geography, University of Nottingham, Nottingham, NG7 2RD

INTRODUCTION

Woodland in the Landscape was the theme of a conference held in October 1997, organised by the PLACE Research Centre at the University College of Ripon & York St. John. The Research Centre is dedicated to the study of *People, Landscape and Cultural Environment*, and all three elements were involved in the conference theme. Woodlands are cultural and economic artefacts as well as natural habitats and features within the landscape. They have supplied timber, wood, pasture, amenity and inspiration to countless generations, both in the past, when they dominated the British landscape, and today, when the surviving fragments of ancient woodland together with their modern counterparts form a link with our rural past and a valued part of our natural heritage. The conference took a temporal perspective, seeking to show how research into historic woodlands has informed our present understanding and can offer a basis for future management and conservation of the woodland resource.

Over two hundred people gathered in York for the conference, including academics, professional foresters, land managers, naturalists and local historians. The speakers were also drawn from a variety of academic, professional and amateur backgrounds, and the interaction between them was one of the strengths of the conference. As well as oral presentations, there were several poster displays, some of which are reproduced in summary form in the Appendix. The event provided an opportunity for an exchange of views between those who manage woodlands and those who study them from an academic perspective. It also revealed the wealth of research work being undertaken on all aspects of woodlands, from studies of their spread in response to environmental change in the early post-glacial (Holocene), through detailed reconstructions of medieval woodland management techniques, to research into people's perceptions of woodlands and forests and their role in sustaining the quality of life.

In the first chapter in this book, **Huntley** focuses on *The Post-glacial History of British Woodlands* in their wider European context. The climate of most of the British Isles is suitable for woodland development and the affinities of the majority of our woodlands are with the temperate deciduous broad-leaved forests of northern Europe. However, in the Scottish Highlands and in south-west Ireland, woodlands have developed which resemble respectively the more northerly coniferous forests and the evergreen broad-leaved woods of south-west Europe. Although post-glacial woodlands have similarities to those which developed in previous interglacials, it is the particular characteristics of the Holocene woodlands which tend to colour our feelings of 'naturalness'. Using pollen analysis as his main tool, Huntley traces the spread of tree species from their glacial refugia in continental Europe and shows how different species had different speeds of colonisation and different patterns of

1

spread, according to their climatic preferences. Most were able to colonise the British Isles via land bridges with the continent which existed in the Early Holocene, but some, such as beech (*Fagus sylvatica*), had to cross a sea barrier to reach these shores. One thing is certain: the early post-glacial woodlands were unlike any found in Europe today in the detail of their species composition.

Later changes to woodland distributions and characteristics were the result of competition between tree species, climatic changes, diseases (eg. in the case of the Elm Decline about 5000 years ago) and human activities. The last factor was ultimately the most significant in reducing woodland cover to a small fraction of its former range and changing the composition of the remaining woodlands. Huntley ends by speculating on the future of British woodlands in the light of global warming. The Scottish pine forests could well become casualties of this climatic change, whereas south-western Britain may become more suitable for broad-leaved evergreen trees, such as the holm oak (*Quercus ilex*). Sadly, there is unlikely to be much expansion of our native mixed woodlands; rather, Huntley envisages plantations of fast-growing willows (*Salix* spp) and poplars (*Populus* spp) being grown for fuel and to counteract the effects of global warming. He sees a bleak future for our semi-natural woodlands.

Pollen analysis, archaeological fieldwork and documentary evidence are all needed to elucidate the details of human impact on the woodlands of specific areas. In a detailed study of *Wood Pasture and the Woodland Economy in Medieval Swaledale* (Chapter 2), **Fleming** uses archaeological and place-name evidence to identify medieval common pastures, including wood pastures. Later field boundaries are set within this older framework. Pollarded trees are a survival from the wood pasture tradition and include elms (*Ulmus* spp), birches (*Betula* spp), hollies (*Ilex aquifolium*), ashes (*Fraxinus excelsior*) and alders (*Alnus glutinosa*). Fleming discusses the origins of pollarded trees and their uses in medieval and later times. It is unlikely, he argues, that mature trees in the 'wildwood' were pollarded, as it would have been more practical to select young trees and manage them for this specific purpose, whether within a woodland or parkland context or as individual trees near settlements. Fleming speculates that early medieval Swaledale was more wooded than Roman Swaledale, as a result of the post-Roman decrease in population, which allowed secondary woodland to spread. The use of trees for leaf-fodder is attested by documentary references from the fourteenth century onwards. Other uses for the products of pollards included fuel, lead-smelting and boundary marking. Later changes in management converted some wood pastures to coppiced woods and led to the replacement of others by arable land or open pasture.

Research into the past distribution and management of woodlands leads naturally to the topic of modern conservation of woodlands. Chapter 3 draws on research into past woodland management to inform decisions about present-day management. In *Judging Woodland Management by Tradition or by Results*,

Kirby argues that traditional management, especially coppicing, will continue to be important and should increase in extent, but he cautions that we need to tailor the precise management to the particular sites, species and features which we are trying to conserve, rather than applying standardised techniques everywhere. We also need to monitor results so that we can learn from our mistakes. He advocates the use of a wide range of treatments, including minimum intervention in some areas. Restoration of coppicing is not necessarily always the right answer, even in woods which were coppiced in the past. This is partly because of a lack of information about the precise treatments used in the past and partly because of changes to the woods themselves and their surrounding landscapes since coppicing ended. The survival of species of particular interest may not relate directly to coppicing but to other factors, such as microclimate, lack of competition, presence of dead wood or other microhabitats. Kirby stresses that each wood is unique and therefore requires its own conservation objectives and management strategy.

The keynote speaker at the conference was **Rackham**, who spoke on *Woodland Conservation: Past, Present and Future.* In Chapter 4, he argues that the sparsity of references to woodland conservation in medieval times was because it was common and taken for granted rather than because it was not practised. Compensation for the paucity of documentary references is offered by the wealth of archaeological evidence, such as wood banks marking former coppice compartments. Many woodlands can be traced back to Anglo-Saxon times, when the distinction between woodland and wood pasture was already well established. Rackham estimates that about 15% of England was wooded in 1086 but only about 6% by 1350, following an intensive period of population growth and agricultural expansion. Some losses were in areas under Forest Law, which gave protection mainly to deer rather than to the trees. Private parks also incurred considerable losses, but common lands often fared better, as trees were usually conserved by communal agreement.

In later centuries, conservation was the result of industrial uses of timber and wood, for instance for charcoal production or shipbuilding. Wood pastures fell victim to remodelling of the landscape, although individual ancient trees often survived. It was the demise of traditional industries which led to the neglect of woodland management in the nineteenth century, paving the way for extensive grubbing out or replanting with conifers in the second part of the twentieth century. Between 1950 and 1975, nearly half the remaining ancient woodland was lost. Nevertheless, several thousand ancient woods still survive today, and Rackham thinks their prospects are now good. Most present-day threats are to non-woodland habitats, and both official and voluntary organisations are actively involved in the conservation of woodlands and veteran trees. However, he is sceptical about some of their efforts, such as the trend towards restoring 'wildwood', as the context for the original woodland ecosystems has been lost. On the other hand, he does not object to the principle of restoring coppicing, on the grounds that wildlife intolerant of disturbance will have left the sites long ago. However, he is pessimistic about the chances of success, mainly because of the problem of deer browsing. Like Kirby, he advocates an individualistic approach to the management of sites, in the light of their known history and particular interest.

Rackham ends by reminding us of the impossibility of distinguishing between the ecological and cultural aspects of woodland conservation. There have been many fashions in conservation. His harshest words are reserved for modern professional conservationists, who tend to follow received dogmas they were taught in college and lack long-term knowledge of the sites on the ground. He also has some hard-hitting comments about generalised strategies and short-term management plans. His warnings about the triumph of 'professionalism' over experience should be read by all those concerned with the conservation management of British woodlands.

In Chapter 5, **Jones** writes about *The Coal Measure Woodlands of South Yorkshire: Past, Present and Future.* He charts the evolution of woodland management on the Coal Measures, examines the characteristic features of the main forms of woodland management in the past, and considers the present condition of surviving woods and prospects for their future. The first real evidence of human impact on the wildwood is from Anglo-Saxon and Scandinavian place-names. These, together with the evidence of medieval settlements, show the difference between the continuously wooded Lower and Middle Coal Measures and the less densely wooded on the Upper Coal Measures and Magnesian Limestone, which were cleared at an earlier date. By Domesday, only perhaps 13% of South Yorkshire was still wooded, compared with about 6% today, with the Coal Measures having slightly higher figures of 15% and 10% respectively. Wood pastures outnumbered coppice woods by 102 to 7, the latter being mainly confined to the Magnesian Limestone belt. Jones argues that population on the Coal Measures was relatively sparse, so demand for wood was less and woods were not fenced. In the more densely populated Magnesian Limestone areas it was important to keep animals out of the woods, because of the greater demand for wood products.

As the population grew in succeeding centuries, the situation gradually changed, and coppicing or coppice-with-standards spread as a means of conserving valuable wood supplies. Jones examines the details of coppicing cycles and the uses of wood for South Yorkshire estates from documentary records. Other rich sources of information are prosecutions for theft or trespass and records of payments for grazing or carrying out hedging or wall repairs. A special type of woodland management was the use of 'holly hags' as winter fodder, as seen also in Swaledale (Chapter 2). Wood pastures, deer parks, chases and commons are also considered.

The decline of traditional management began in the late Middle Ages but reached a peak in the eighteenth and nineteenth centuries. In South Yorkshire, the use of coke rather than charcoal as fuel for the rapidly expanding iron and steel industries led to the decrease of the coppicing tradition and its replacement by plantation forestry. The sites of many ancient woods can still be located, even when under modern housing estates, and here and there a few remnants of trees or ground flora survive to remind us of the woodland past. Others have survived as high forest, game coverts or modern plantations, but often with dense, even-aged trees and impoverished shrub and ground flora layers. Contemporary problems include the dark, uninteresting aspect of many woods, reducing their value for amenity - a theme explored at greater length by Simon Bell in Chapter 10. The reintroduction of active management has also caused some problems, as noted also by Rackham (Chapter 4). In the last two decades, however, more positive management by local authorities and countryside agencies has led to the development of multi-purpose forests and revitalisation of some local industries using woodland products. The future for South Yorkshire's woodlands now looks brighter, provided current initiatives can be sustained.

Two chapters explore the historic woodlands of North Yorkshire, using documentary evidence. **Gledhill** has made a detailed study of *Medieval Woodland in North Yorkshire* (Chapter 6). He provides an overview of woodland distribution and management in the county, focusing on the limitations and challenges of interpreting the evidence. His sources of information include place-names, Domesday Book, medieval charters, monastic chartularies and various documents relating to the ownership of land. Only certain place-name elements may be used as reliable indicators of woodland or woodland clearance. The problems of using Domesday Book to reconstruct former woodland distributions are well known, and North Yorkshire provides excellent exemplification of the limitations of the evidence, such as the uncertainties over translating Domesday figures into modern areal measurements. Woodland in some areas, such as the North York Moors, tends to be over-estimated in Domesday Book, whereas hardly any information exists for others, eg. Craven. Bearing in mind the limitations of the evidence, several distinct woodland landscapes may be distinguished. The Vale of Mowbray, Vale of Pickering and the Yorkshire Wolds were largely cleared of woodland cover by Domesday (and possibly by the end of Roman times), whereas the Vale of York, parts of the Howardian Hills and the western fringes of the North York Moors appear still to have been well wooded. In the Pennine Dales and other parts of the North York Moors, woodland was probably confined to the steeper valley sides.

The terminology used for different types of woodland in medieval times reveals the types of management in operation. It is clear that wood pasture was by far the most important use of woodland in early medieval times throughout North Yorkshire. However, in later centuries there was a shift towards coppice management, which Gledhill describes as a revolution in woodland management between 1400 and 1550. As a result of this change, most woodlands which survive today show signs of former coppicing, even though during the early Medieval period this was not the traditional form of management. The traditions of common wood pasture management survived longest in the Vale of York, which is the focus for Chapter 7.

Jennifer Kaner and the Yorkshire Philosophical Society's Woodland History Group have been making a detailed study of *Historic Woodland in the Vale of York*. The city of York was surrounded on all sides by Forests in the early medieval period but much of the area was disafforested early, as local inhabitants chose to pay to be rid of Forest Law. Kaner cites fascinating details of the uses of woodland products, including for building timber, bark and faggots, and of the methods of transport and prices paid. Woodlands within the area decreased in extent during the medieval period, but those which remained were more carefully managed to provide building timber and wood for fuel and other uses. The details of the story for the Vale of York are traced down to the present day, including changes in woodland ownership and management priorities. Kaner reminds us that the survival of woods has always depended on their being valued and used. In the past this was for timber and wood; now more commonly they are used for hunting or game preserves.

Recent research has recognised the importance of microhabitats within woodlands for their nature conservation interest. This is the theme of Chapter 8, in which **Watkins** and **Lavers** write on *Losing one's head in Sherwood Forest: the Dead Wood Resource of the Ancient Oaks.* They have surveyed the ancient oaks of part of Sherwood Forest to make an inventory of the dead wood habitat, which involved examining over 1500 trees. The Forest is steeped in history; the oldest trees are estimated to be at least 1000 years old. There was no tradition of coppicing in Sherwood Forest but historical records exist for pollarding, although few traces remain. Over half the trees surveyed were dead and many of the living ones had lost their crowns, so they form a valuable dead wood resource for wildlife from woodpeckers to wood-boring beetles and fungi. Interestingly, the turn-over of trees is very slow; only five trees died between 1991 and 1996. Watkins and Lavers discuss the problems of methodology and the implications of the dead wood resource for future management and conservation.

The last two contributions to the conference focused on the non-materialistic side of woodlands and their role in the landscapes of the future. **Morag Bell** and **Lois Child** examine the contribution of the National Forest to the contemporary debates over the quality of life and the relationship between human society and nature, in their chapter entitled *Redesigning a Region: the National Forest and the Quality of Life*. Issues include the health of the nation, the concept of citizenship and landscape design. The National Forest is an ambitious project, incorporating conservation and environmental regeneration of former industrial land in the East Midlands. Trees have been used for centuries to provide a stabilising influence in times of rapid social change. They have acquired political and ethical dimensions, both at home and abroad. Both enhancing the physical environment and rehabilitating society were important themes underpinning the 1995 White Paper on Rural England. The National Forest concept was also embedded in the UK responses to the Rio Summit.

A multi-purpose future for the National Forest is envisaged. It is hoped that it will promote an English woodland tradition and involve widespread public access, including access for disabled people. The chapter gives details of schemes which have been undertaken or are planned and examines conflicts of interest which arise in their execution. Progress with planting has been disappointing in the first ten years; perhaps the new millennium will give it the boost it needs?

In the last chapter, **Simon Bell** looks at recent research on *Woodland in the Landscape*. He examines the perceptual and aesthetic responses of the public to new woodlands, and looks at people's relationships with woodlands in the landscape as well as with woodlands as individual features. He traces the historical associations of the British people with woodland and forest - associations which still shape our thinking today, for example in attitudes towards the National Forest or Community Forests. Bell reviews research into the types of woodland landscapes the public prefer, the landscape value of farm woods, perceptions of fear and safety in woods, the psychological effects of the woodland experience on people's lives, and the benefits of making improvements in woodlands.

Using questionnaires, interviews and responses to photographic images, the researchers tested people's views, looking for differences linked to age, sex, race or socio-economic group. The research revealed different attitudes between the general public, landowners and professional foresters or landscape architects. It also showed different associations in people's minds between 'wood' and 'forest', revealing a general preference for broad-leaved woodland and more natural-looking, irregular woodland designs. Woodland is seen as an integral part of the landscape, not as a separate component of it.

In the final chapter, **Butlin** draws together the general themes of the conference and relates them to the wider field of woodland research in Britain and abroad. He presents a personal overview of the subject and points to some priorities for future research work. **Poster presentations** covered several topics related to the general theme of the conference, including the work of the York Archaeological Wood Centre, indicator and invader species amongst woodland plants, the use of GIS to explore the distribution of woodlands and hedgerows in Hampshire, the relevance of landscape history to a vision of forest management, and the role of the Farming and Wildlife Advisory Group in giving woodland advice.

I should like to thank all the speakers and presenters at the conference for their time and trouble in preparing material for publication. Many staff and students of the University College of Ripon & York St. John gave freely of their time to assist with the smooth running of the conference, which contributed greatly to the success of the event. I am also grateful to staff at the Leeds University Press for their swift and efficient handling of this publication. I hope that we have done justice in this book to the work of the authors and that those who read it will enjoy the fruits of their labours. It would be difficult to underestimate the role which woodlands have played in the past in Britain. It is to be hoped that, through research such as that recorded in this book, future generations will be inspired to value and cherish our woodland heritage.

Margaret Atherden.
September 1998.

Chapter 1

The Post-glacial History of British Woodlands

Brian Huntley

Overture

In order to understand and evaluate the history of the woodlands of the British Isles since the end of the last glacial stage, some ten thousand years ago, we must begin by placing this history in an appropriate geographical and temporal context. The appropriate context is geographically the whole of the continent of Europe and temporally the late Quaternary geological period. At the present time, the geographical context of our forests is that they lie predominantly in the extensive area of winter-deciduous temperate broad-leaved forests that are the potential natural vegetation cover of much of Europe north of the Alps and south of the Boreal zone. That is to say that climatically most of the land area of the British Isles is suitable for the development of such forests; the key exceptions to this generalisation are our highest and most exposed mountains, some exposed coastal areas, upland and western areas with extensive blanket peat cover, and areas of unsuitable soils that are too shallow or infertile to support forest development. In addition, some of our northern uplands, and much of Scotland north of the Highland Boundary Fault, experience climatic conditions of a more Boreal character: these areas would naturally support forests dominated by either Boreal broad-leaved deciduous trees, Boreal needle-leaved conifers, or a mixture of the two. Similarly, in a narrow zone close to the south-western coasts of both Britain and Ireland, the extremely oceanic climate has closer affinities with conditions in the Atlantic fringes of south-west Europe: here the relative freedom from frost naturally favours the dominance of broad-leaved evergreen trees.

The temporal context of our post-glacial forests is, at its simplest, that they represent forest development during the latest of the series of interglacial periods that have punctuated the late Quaternary at intervals of approximately one hundred thousand years. Perhaps more important, however, is the realisation that for a large part, probably the majority, of the last eight hundred thousand years the environment of the British Isles has been unsuitable for the growth of trees and the

9

development of forests. Linked to this is an awareness that the British Isles have, nonetheless, been forested many times before both during previous interglacials, when climate was broadly comparable to that of the post-glacial and of the present, and during interstadials, intervals characterised by a climate intermediate between that of fully glacial times and present climate. At the last glacial maximum, fifteen to twenty-five thousand years ago, an ice sheet covered much of the British Isles. This ice sheet extended south as far as south Wales, the English Midlands and north Norfolk; those areas to the south not covered by ice experienced a severe climate that was suitable only for the development of tundra-like vegetation on a landscape subject to disturbance by freeze–thaw cycles and within which a variety of landforms and structures associated with permafrost, e.g. pingos and ice wedges, developed (Jones & Keen, 1993).

Prior to the last glacial maximum, during a period of almost fifty thousand years, the earth experienced repeated climatic fluctuations that were perhaps expressed at their greatest magnitude in the British Isles. During the cold extremes of these fluctuations conditions probably were climatically as severe as during the glacial maximum, whereas during the warm extremes the sparse full-glacial vegetation was replaced by a more continuous cover that in parts was apparently of a shrub-tundra character. We must, however, go back to the more marked climatic fluctuations following the last interglacial to discover evidence of forests in Britain; at that time, during an interstadial period centred around one hundred thousand years ago, Norway Spruce (*Picea abies*) was present in forests of a Boreal character in the English Midlands. To find forests comparable to those of the post-glacial and dominated by temperate broad-leaved trees we must go back even further, to the last (Ipswichian – GB; Eemian – European mainland) interglacial, a period of perhaps ten to twelve thousand years centred around one hundred and twenty-five thousand years ago. However, although the forests of that time were similar in general character to those of the post-glacial, they exhibited a number of striking floristic differences, notably the presence of the Montpelier Maple (*Acer monspessulanum*), a tree found today only as far north as central France, and the extreme dominance of Hornbeam (*Carpinus betulus*) during the later part of the interglacial. This same general pattern is seen if we go back further and examine the composition of the forests that developed in the British Isles during earlier interglacials. The forests of each such interval have exhibited important differences either in their composition, or in the species that have dominated, or in both; the later part of the Gortian (Hoxnian – GB; Holsteinian – European mainland) interglacial of Ireland, for example, had forests dominated by Silver Fir (*Abies alba*) and Yew (*Taxus baccata*) accompanied in the understorey by Rhododendron (*Rhododendron ponticum*) and Box (*Buxus* sp.) (Godwin, 1975; Mitchell, 1976).

Thus, as the post-glacial history of the forests of the British Isles unfolds, we must not forget that this is simply the most recent variation upon a theme of which many variations have been played before. Our Holocene woodlands are only one manifestation of forest cover in the British Isles, yet they strongly influence our view of the native *versus* exotic status of woody species. They are, however, destined to inevitable change, whether naturally on time scales of millennia or tens of millennia as the natural pacemaker of variations in the earth's orbit around the sun causes inescapable changes in the global climate, or more precipitately as a consequence of more immediate changes in the global climate brought about by the activities of the human population as it destroys global forests, burns fossil fuels and generally degrades our global environment. Whatever their uncertain future, however, the task for now is to understand their past, and the starting point for this is the end of the last glacial maximum, around fifteen thousand years ago, as global ice sheets began rapidly to melt.

Prelude — *The landscape revealed*
Although much of the landscape of the British Isles had been ice-covered at the last glacial maximum, these ice sheets melted rapidly during the earlier stages of deglaciation so that it seems likely that little vestige of them remained by around thirteen thousand years ago. As they melted a landscape was uncovered that in upland Britain especially is characterised by glacially-moulded U-shaped valleys, corries, roche-moutonnées, etc. as well as a variety of moraines and other depositional features. In lowland areas the predominant legacy of the ice sheets is the extensive deposits of boulder clay, and of fluvio-glacial sands and gravels. Even where the ice had not extended, the melting of the permafrost left behind disturbed landscapes.

This initially barren and disturbed landscape was rapidly colonised by plants and animals, a process that was perhaps facilitated by the persistence at this time of a broad land connection between eastern Britain and continental Europe. Whereas some of the early colonists included apparently warmth-demanding beetles, trees were relatively slow to arrive. This perhaps in part reflected their remote areas of distribution during the glacial maximum. The only trees that persisted north of the Alps at that time apparently were Boreal species – Birch (*Betula* spp.), Aspen (*Populus tremula*) and Scots Pine (*Pinus sylvestris*). Further east Larch (*Larix* sp.) was present in Poland, and in Russia Norway Spruce may have formed forests of a Boreal character. The broad-leaved deciduous trees, however, were restricted to limited areas in the mountains of southern Europe, especially in the southern Balkans, Italy and southern Iberia (Huntley & Birks, 1983; Huntley, 1988; Huntley, 1990b; Huntley & Prentice, 1993).

Such remoteness alone nonetheless may not account for the initial absence of trees; the climate of that time apparently was more markedly seasonal, so that whereas the summer conditions may have been as warm or warmer than those of today, winter conditions were more severe. Such severity may account for the persistence of many Arctic–Alpine elements in the flora as well as for the initial absence of trees. As the severity of the winter conditions declined, however, the Boreal trees did expand their range north-westwards across Europe during this so-called late-glacial interstadial (Fig. 1.1). It is apparent from finds of macrofossils of their fruits and catkin scales that Birch trees certainly were present in Britain twelve thousand years ago, their range extending northwards at least as far as Aberdeenshire. Aspen, Willows (*Salix* spp.) and Juniper (*Juniperus communis*) all also were present, and there even is evidence in the form of macrofossils indicating that Scots Pine may have been present, albeit sparsely and locally. Other trees and shrubs also probably were widely, if sparsely, present, notably Rowan (*Sorbus aucuparia*), both macrofossils and pollen of which have been recorded from a small number of localities during this interval.

Figure 1.1: Late-glacial and early post-glacial history of birch and pine
A: Birch (*Betula*); B: Pine (*Pinus*). Threshold isopolls (25%) for 12,000, 11,000, 10,000 and 9,000 radiocarbon years before present (simplified from Huntley & Birks, 1983).

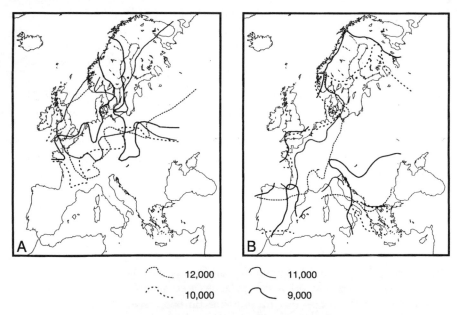

> ~~~ 12,000   ⌒ 11,000
> ·· ·· 10,000   ⌒ 9,000

Despite the presence of this variety of Boreal trees during the late-glacial interstadial, it seems unlikely that any part of the British Isles was extensively covered by dense forests. Birch woodlands of a sub-Arctic character may have covered southern Britain, but further north the tree cover apparently was sparse and discontinuous. Furthermore, the climate was already deteriorating; evidence of a short interval of severe conditions just after twelve thousand years ago can be seen in some palaeoecological records and forms the basis for a sub-division of the late-glacial interstadial into three – an initial period of warmest summer conditions, the Bölling, separated from a second warm period with less seasonal climate, the Alleröd, by two centuries or so of severe conditions, the Older Dryas. Climatic conditions continued to cool during the millennium preceding eleven thousand years ago; after eleven thousand years ago there was a rapid global climate change with severe cooling around the North Atlantic especially. Conditions in the British Isles during the subsequent Younger Dryas interval were once again unsuitable for the presence of trees. An extensive ice sheet developed in the Western Highlands of Scotland, and elsewhere in the mountains of eastern and northern Scotland, the English Lake District, Wales and Ireland local corrie glaciers developed. This revertence to near glacial climate conditions lasted for between five hundred and one thousand years. It forms the basis for an overall tripartite sub-division of the late-glacial, within which is embedded the secondary tripartite sub-division of the late-glacial interstadial. In this scheme the interval between the initial melting of the glacial ice sheets and the arrival of the first organisms indicative of a warm climate is the Oldest Dryas; this precedes the late-glacial interstadial that then is followed by the Younger Dryas.

The late-glacial period came to an abrupt end with the rapid climatic warming that marked the onset of the post-glacial stage some ten thousand years ago. Prior to this, however, it seems likely that the climate had shown minor fluctuations toward warmer conditions; the extensive areas of 'hummocky moraine' in many Western Highland glens apparently indicate that the Younger Dryas ice sheet had become stagnant before finally melting away. Such instability seems to characterise the climate during most of the late-glacial period, as well as during the preceding glacial stage, and it is likely that as more comes to be known we will discover that the often-used tripartite sub-divisions outlined above are too simplistic and mask a more complicated sequence of events.

Fugue — *Arrival of the trees*
With the transition to the post-glacial, ten thousand years ago, the tempo of vegetation change increased. Although the Boreal trees that reached the British Isles during the late-glacial interstadial were once again generally the first to arrive, especially Birch and Scots Pine, they were swiftly being overtaken by several of the more temperate, warmth-demanding trees. These trees had, even during the late-glacial interstadial, been distributed only in southern Europe. They were, however, able to extend their ranges northwards at extraordinarily rapid rates, averaging as much as two kilometres per year in extreme cases. The first to arrive included Oak (*Quercus* spp.), Elm (*Ulmus* spp.), Hazel (*Corylus avellana*) and Alder (*Alnus glutinosa*) (Fig. 1.2), although the latter initially remained restricted in distribution (Huntley & Birks, 1983; Birks, 1989).

Figure 1.2: Early post-glacial history of oak, elm, hazel and alder
A: Oak (*Quercus*); B: Elm (*Ulmus*); C: Hazel (*Corylus avellana*); D: Alder (*Alnus*). Threshold isopolls (2%) for 10,000, 9,000, 8,000 and 6,000 radiocarbon years before present (simplified from Huntley & Birks, 1983).

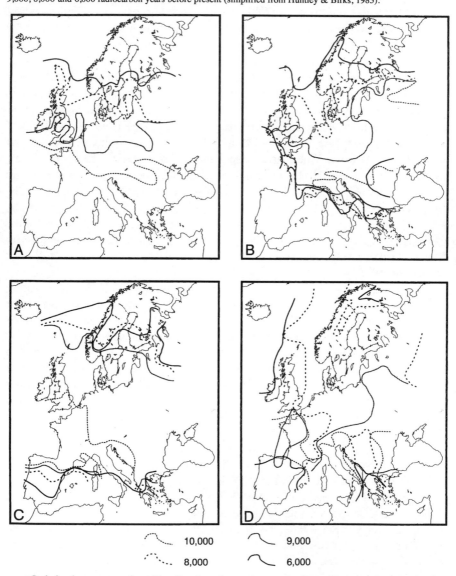

```
⌒⌒⌢  10,000      ⌒⌒  9,000
⌒⌒⋅⋅  8,000       ⌒⌒  6,000
```

Oak had an extensive distribution throughout southern Europe during the last glacial, and was widespread and abundant there during the late-glacial. With the arrival of the post-glacial it expanded rapidly northwards in the west, reaching south-west England already within five hundred years and other areas adjacent to the Irish Sea by nine thousand years ago. Within a further thousand years it was established throughout the British Isles. It seems probable that this history was shared by the two species of Oak native to the British Isles; recent genetic evidence indicates that both Sessile Oak (*Q. petraea*) and Pedunculate Oak (*Q. robur*) expanded northwards through western France from populations that had been distributed in the Iberian peninsula during the last glacial.

Elm apparently had a more scattered distribution in southern and eastern Europe during the last glacial, and remained relatively restricted during the late-glacial. Its subsequent history of post-glacial range expansion is more complicated than that of Oak, perhaps indicating that the five species today native in Europe had markedly differing glacial areas of distribution. Of these five, only two are now considered native to the British Isles, 'Small Elm' (*U. minor*) and Wych Elm (*U. glabra*). Ten thousand years ago Elm was increasing in abundance in south-east Europe, and in another five hundred years it had become widespread and abundant in that region but was only just extending its range north of the Alps *via* the Danube lowlands. By nine thousand years ago, however, it was established in areas around the Irish Sea, apparently either from a quite separate source population, or else having spread very rapidly northwards through France but at low density. Unlike Oak, it had not at that time increased in abundance in western France; indeed its abundance remained relatively limited in that area throughout the post-glacial.

By eight thousand five hundred years ago Elm was present as far north as southern Scotland, although a further fifteen hundred years were to pass before it reached its northernmost post-glacial limits in northern Scotland. During these same two millennia a tongue of higher Elm abundance extended northward across eastern France and into south-east England; it is tempting to suggest that this represents the range expansion of the second native species. If this speculation has any substance, then it seems most probable that the initial arrival in the British Isles was Wych Elm, and that it reached the area around the Irish Sea by expansion from a population that had been present in the far west of Europe, perhaps in areas now below sea level, during the last glacial. The contrasting present distributional limits of 'Small Elm' and Wych Elm provide circumstantial support for this inference; whereas 'Small Elm' has a northern limit that trends from south-west to north-east and reaches its northern native limit in Gotland, Wych Elm extends furthest north in western Norway, to more than 67°N, and exhibits a north-west to south-east trend in its northern limit, barely reaching 60°N at 60°E. Wych Elm thus is an excellent candidate for a species that might have reached its northern limit during the last glacial somewhere along the western continental margin, perhaps even on exposed areas of the continental shelf south of Ireland or west of Brittany.

Hazel is another species that today exhibits a north-west to south-east trending northern limit, extending further north even than Wych Elm in western Norway but hardly reaching 60°E at all. It may not be coincidental that it too expanded first into southern and south-western England, although like Oak it also was present at comparable abundance in western France. In contrast to both Oak and Elm, however, it was no more than sparsely and locally present in southern Europe in the late-glacial pollen record, yet it also showed the most rapid increase, being present in both France and southern England almost immediately after the transition to the post-glacial. Thereafter its range expansion continued to be amongst the most rapid, and it also became at least temporarily the most abundant woody taxon in the pollen record of much of western Europe. Within five hundred years it had expanded as far north as southern Scotland and by nine thousand years ago it was abundant throughout all parts of the British Isles except the Scottish Highlands, where it took another millennium to reach peak abundance.

Alder, the last of this group of trees, all of which reached the British Isles during the first two millennia of the post-glacial, has a strikingly different history from any of the foregoing. During the late-glacial period it was widely present, and even locally abundant, especially in mountainous areas of southern Europe. Immediately following the transition to the post-glacial there is evidence that it increased and became locally abundant in north-west France; within the next five hundred years or so it apparently became established at a number of coastal and estuarine sites, as well as at some favourable inland sites such as valley mires, in southern and western Britain. Unlike the preceding three taxa, however, Alder did not then extend throughout the landscape and become a component of the early post-glacial forests. Instead, for the next fifteen hundred years or so it remained localised to these coastal and wetland sites. Only around eight thousand years ago did it begin to increase in abundance more generally and to become a more widespread forest component; anomalously this expansion on to the landscape began first in south-east England, where it represented the western edge of a general pattern of westward expansion. Subsequently, Alder increased in abundance throughout the British Isles during the next three millennia; most of England was occupied by seven thousand years ago, by six thousand years ago it had reached the far north and west of Scotland, and the last area to be occupied thereafter was the far west of Ireland (Chambers & Price, 1985; Bennett & Birks, 1990).

It is tempting to speculate about the origins of this 'two stage' expansion of Alder. The first stage seems to closely parallel the behaviour of Elm and Hazel, and thus may represent expansion from a population that was distributed on the Atlantic fringe of Europe during the last glacial. This population, however, apparently was unable to expand beyond limited favourable sites. This limitation might reflect a climatic limitation of the species to such sites at that time, or alternatively might reflect a genetic limitation of the populations of the species present at that time such that they were incapable of occupying the full range of sites suitable for the species. Were the former hypothesis true, then the subsequent secondary expansion on to the wider landscape would result from a climatic change, whereas were the latter hypothesis to hold, then the secondary expansion would reflect the arrival in the

British Isles of a second population of immigrants differing in genetic makeup from the initial colonists. Given that Alder favours heavy or peaty soils prone to waterlogging, and that the initial stage of expansion was on to favourable sites where topographic conditions would induce waterlogged conditions, the most logical climatic change that would enable expansion on to the wider landscape would be a general shift toward cooler and/or wetter conditions.

The prevailing circulation patterns in mid-latitudes result in a marked west–east gradient of precipitation across Europe, whilst the land–sea contrast in thermal capacity results in a strong west–east trend of increasing seasonal temperature contrasts, with the mean temperature of the warmest month at the present day being comparable in the English Midlands to that in Rovaniemi, the 'capital' of Finnish Lapland. If these climatic patterns were broadly comparable during the early post-glacial, then it is extremely difficult, if not impossible, to envisage a scenario that would bring about a change toward cooler and/or wetter conditions first in the north and east of Europe and only later in the west. However, the climatic patterns may not have been comparable; in particular, the enhanced northern hemisphere summer insolation is likely to have caused a poleward shift of the major circulation features. This might well have resulted in the prevalent summer storm track being shifted northward such that the British Isles received less summer rainfall than at the present. Combined with the higher evapo-transpirational demand that would have resulted from the warmer summer temperatures and higher insolation, the net effect would have been generally drier soils. In this context, two observations are important: firstly, the geographical distribution of Alder becomes sparse and discontinuous in the Iberian peninsula at the present day as the tree becomes increasingly restricted to the most favourable sites for topographically induced waterlogging; and secondly, Holm Oak (*Quercus ilex*), a drought-tolerant tree that has the centre of its distribution today in the Mediterranean region, spread rapidly northward through western France during the first two millennia of the post glacial. Thus, we cannot exclude the hypothesis that the rapid expansion of Alder into Fennoscandia during the first two millennia of the post-glacial, and its later and slower expansion across the landscapes of the British Isles and western mainland Europe, was a response to climatic change.

The alternative hypothesis can only be tested by examining the genetics of present populations of Alder. In particular, the partitioning of genetic variability both at the scale of the landscape and across the species' entire European range would need to be investigated in order to evaluate the potential for two genetically, and consequently adaptively, distinct sub-populations to have separately expanded across Europe during the post-glacial.

Before leaving the early post-glacial it is appropriate finally to consider the consequences of these rapid range expansions in terms of the resulting spatio-temporal patterns of forest composition. Perhaps the first point to note is that Birch woodlands were the first to occupy virtually all parts of the British Isles, although the period for which they subsequently endured varied considerably. In the south-east Scots Pine very soon followed the Birch and mixed Pine–Birch forests of a relatively Boreal character developed. Further north the Birch grew with Willows and Juniper and the woodlands had a sub-Arctic character. The northward expansion of Scots Pine into these sub-Arctic woodlands was overtaken within the first millennium of the post-glacial by the rapidly expanding Hazel, and soon thereafter also by Oak and Elm. Mixed forests of Scots Pine, Birch and Hazel temporarily were extensive in northern England; similar forests also were found at this time in Denmark and southern parts of Sweden and Norway. Further north Hazel expanded into areas occupied only by Birch, forming Birch–Hazel woodlands that were not mirrored extensively elsewhere in Europe. Oak–Elm forests with Hazel rapidly occupied areas adjacent to the southern part of the Irish Sea, and by eight thousand years ago had extended to occupy most of the British Isles. An important feature of these forest types is that they have either no, or at least no spatially-extensive, modern analogue; that is to say that they differed in composition from the modern forests of Europe (Huntley, 1990b; Huntley, 1990a).

Minuet — *Ever-changing forests*
Eight thousand years ago the British Isles already were extensively covered by forests of broad-leaved, winter-deciduous trees, and thus by forests similar, at least in terms of their structure and the functional type of trees by which they were dominated, to the present potential forest cover of most of the area of these islands. These forests differed from the present-day potential forests, however, in their floristic composition, and also covered a larger part of the British Isles than they potentially would cover today. Although the tempo of change had slowed somewhat, it had not ceased. The forests of the British Isles continued to receive new immigrants, and to alter in composition and spatial pattern, as the post-glacial climate continued to change.

Amongst the trees strikingly absent from Britain eight thousand years ago were Small-leaved Lime (*Tilia cordata*), Beech (*Fagus sylvatica*) and Hornbeam (*Carpinus betulus*), whilst others, including Ash (*Fraxinus excelsior*) and Yew (*Taxus baccata*), either were absent or were present only very sparsely. Scots Pine also was apparently an uncommon tree at that time, nowhere acting as a forest dominant.

Small-leaved Lime expanded its range steadily across Europe during the early post-glacial, although at rates much slower than those attained by Elm and Hazel. It apparently was distributed in the mountains of southern Europe during the last glacial and expanded its range north-westwards along a broad front during the early post-glacial. It reached Britain about seven thousand five hundred years ago and thereafter continued its steady north-westward progress so that it reached its maximum extent between six and five thousand years ago when its range limit lay in northern England and corresponded more or less to that seen at the present day. Although, as an insect-pollinated tree, its pollen abundance was always relatively low, it apparently was a major component of the mixed-deciduous forests of England during the mid-post-glacial, perhaps accounting for between one quarter and one half of the trees in the forests of south-east England.

Figure 1.3: Late post-glacial history of hornbeam and beech
A: Hornbeam (*Carpinus betulus*); B: Beech (*Fagus*). Threshold isopolls (hornbeam 1%; beech 2%) for 6,000, 4,000, and 2,000 radiocarbon years before present and for the present day (simplified from Huntley & Birks, 1983).

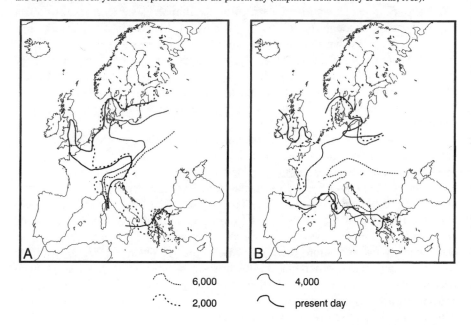

6,000	4,000
2,000	present day

Beech was even later to reach the British Isles, it too having spread north-westwards along a broad front, albeit even more slowly than Small-leaved Lime (Fig 1.3). During the last glacial Beech appears to have been restricted to the mountains of Italy and the Balkans. Initially it expanded its range rather slowly and became only locally abundant; only after seven thousand years ago did it extend its range to the north of the Alps. Thereafter it maintained a steady rate of spread, so that by around three thousand years ago it had reached the north coast of France and had appeared also in south-east England. Whereas earlier immigrants had arrived whilst there still was a land connection between Britain and mainland Europe, the lateness of the arrival of Beech in Britain required that it cross the barrier of the English Channel, which by that time was similar in breadth to the present day. This has led to speculation that humans were involved as the agents of dispersal of its fruits into Britain. However, when the spread into Britain is seen in context as the extreme north-westernmost component of a general range expansion, then it is apparent that it is not necessary to hypothesise such a human involvement. Beech expanded north-westwards across mainland Europe for several millennia at average rates of around 300 m per year. The maintenance of such rates required that fruits were reliably and regularly dispersed distances of 10 to 20 km, given that the trees take several decades to achieve reproductive maturity; dispersal across the 30 km or so necessary to cross the English Channel is no longer such an exceptional event. The most likely agents for dispersal over such distances are birds, such as the Jay (*Garrulus glandarius*), and large carnivorous mammals, such as the Brown Bear (*Ursus arctos*). Although Brown Bears will move distances of 10 km or more in a night, it is less clear whether they are likely to swim across a seaway such as the English Channel. Jays, however, easily would be capable of flying across the English Channel; their relatives the Rook (*Corvus corax*) will fly up to 30 km twice a day in winter when moving between feeding areas and roosting sites (L.R. Griffin, unpublished data). Jays thus might readily have dispersed fruits from France to England.

Insufficient data are available to document any details of the post-glacial range expansions across Europe of Ash and Yew. Both trees were, however, present in parts of southern Europe during the last glacial and both became relatively abundant components of the post-glacial forests of the British Isles only after around five thousand years ago. Whether they too, like Beech, immigrated only after the isolation of the British Isles from mainland Europe is unclear; limited pollen and macrofossil evidence, however, suggests that they may already have been sparsely present before the time of isolation. Hornbeam, however, parallels Beech in many ways, expanding northwards and westwards across Europe even later and apparently arriving in northern France only about fifteen hundred years ago and in Britain shortly thereafter (Fig. 1.3). Here again there is nonetheless some doubt as to whether it may have been sparsely present in many areas, including south-east England, prior to the time of rapid expansion, the latter then representing population rather than range expansion.

Whatever the details of the timing of their immigration and expansion, Beech and Hornbeam apparently remained restricted to the south-east of England, where, however, they came to form characteristic components of the forest cover of that region. In contrast, Ash and Yew swiftly became widespread, both also colonising Ireland.

During the same interval when these trees were expanding their ranges northwards and westwards into Britain, Alder was, as discussed above, extending across the wider landscape and thus it too was adding to the diversity of forest composition in the British Isles. Scots Pine too was on the move at this time, but apparently from an unlikely direction. Having been reduced to a state of relative rarity as its northward expansion was overtaken by that of Hazel, Elm and Oak, it re-emerged as a local forest dominant in the North-west Highlands of Scotland around eight thousand years ago. Subsequently the area of its dominance expanded south-eastwards so that by around five thousand years ago it dominated much of the lower elevation forest cover within the Scottish Highlands (Bennett, 1984). Parallel but more localised expansions also occurred in western Ireland and around the Galloway Hills of south-west Scotland. Around four thousand years ago, and in the space of a century or two, it further expanded its range to the far north coast of Scotland and into the Outer Hebrides, in both areas occurring extensively on blanket peatlands (Wilkins, 1984; Gear & Huntley, 1991; Huntley, Daniell & Allen, 1997). This was, however, a short-lived expansion and within a few centuries it had withdrawn once again to essentially the area within which today we find the remaining fragments of Caledonian pine forest, namely the area where climatic conditions favour the development of such forests rather than forests of broad-leaved temperate trees. It continued to occupy that area thereafter.

The consequence of these ongoing changes in the ranges of trees was that the forest cover of the British Isles became more diverse in floristic composition and at the same time approached more closely in composition and spatial extent the potential forest cover of the present day. It was these forests that then have been subjected to a variety of human influences, but before we move on to this phase in which human impacts upon the forests become a predominant factor, one last event must be mentioned. Around five thousand years ago Elm trees rapidly declined in abundance in the forests of the British Isles. This 'Elm Decline' could in itself form the subject for an entire chapter; suffice it to say that its cause has been the subject of much debate. However, it now seems most probable that the decline was the consequence of an epidemic outbreak of a pathogen specific to Elm – it is tempting to speculate that the pathogen involved was the familiar 'Dutch Elm Disease' fungus (*Ceratocystis ulmae*), vectored then as now by bark beetles (*Scolytus* spp.). This epidemic apparently swept across Europe from south-east to north-west over a period of some two thousand years or so, accelerating as it went and selectively killing and subsequently suppressing the recovery of Elm (Huntley & Birks, 1983). Although no evidence has yet been found of the pathogen, remains of the bark beetles that act as its vector have been found contemporaneous with the decline (Girling, 1988). Following its decline, although locally in some parts of the west it did show temporary recovery, Elm was never again to be as abundant a component of our forests as during the first five millennia of the post-glacial.

Finale — *Human destruction and changes*
Although Mesolithic peoples had perhaps used fire as an agent of deliberate forest management, in particular to maintain open areas beneficial for hunting, their impact upon the forest cover of the British Isles had been limited and localised.

Human impacts became progressively more persistent and extensive following the arrival of Neolithic culture and the associated cultivation of crops and herding of domesticated animals. These activities steadily increased in importance and in their associated impacts during the subsequent Bronze and Iron Ages and had accelerated impacts from Roman times and onward throughout the historic period. The crops introduced and cultivated included a range of alien cereals; initially Emmer (*Triticum dicoccon*) and Bread Wheat (*T. aestivum*) as well as the Hulled form of Six-row Barley (*Hordeum vulgare*) were introduced, and subsequently also the Naked form of Six-row Barley, Spelt (*T. spelta*), Oats (*Avena* spp.) and Rye (*Secale cereale*). The domesticated animals also included alien species; Sheep (*Ovis aries*), Goats (*Capra hircus*), Horses (*Equus caballus*) and Rabbits (*Oryctolagus cuniculus*) were all introductions to the British Isles.

Whereas the principal impact of cultivation was the direct reduction in the extent of forest cover as land was cleared to grow crops, the impact of the domesticated herbivores also included their indirect role in suppressing the regeneration of trees and in reducing the extent and abundance of many grazing-sensitive herbaceous species. Although initially Neolithic cultivation was of a shifting nature, with cleared patches of forest abandoned after only a few growing seasons and allowed to regenerate, progressively the agricultural activities became more settled and their impact upon the natural forest cover more persistent. Forest cover reduction was greatest initially in relatively lowland areas of more readily cultivated soils; later the heavier less easily worked lowland soils too were cultivated. The last areas to suffer from forest cover destruction associated with human activities were the Highlands of Scotland. By the Medieval Period, however, most of the forest cover of the British Isles had been lost; especially in the lowlands only managed fragments generally remained.

In contrast to this progressive reduction in forest cover, and in the occurrence of associated grazing-sensitive herbs, human activities had limited impact upon the composition of forest canopies prior to the seventeenth century. Although some have proposed that human activities *caused* the expansions of the ranges of some trees during the second half of the post-glacial (Behre, 1988), it now is widely accepted that human disturbances of the established forest cover *facilitated* these expansions that were occurring in response to continuing climatic changes (Bradshaw & Hannon, 1992; Björkman & Bradshaw, 1996). The impact of humans upon the composition of forest canopies began when selective management was first practised; the abundance of Oak in many British woodlands, and of Beech in the woodlands of the Chilterns probably reflects in part such selective management, as perhaps does the generally uncommon status of Small-leaved Lime. This impact intensified with the deliberate introduction of alien trees such as Sycamore (*Acer pseudoplatanus*) and has been intense from the seventeenth century onwards as 'plantation' management of woodlands came to be practised. Today many woodlands owe their canopy composition to deliberate planting, and huge areas of the British Isles are covered by artificial forests whose canopies are dominated by, or comprised exclusively of, alien trees, often principally conifers imported from other continents, for example Sitka Spruce (*Picea sitchensis*), Lodgepole Pine (*Pinus contorta*), Western Hemlock (*Tsuga heterophylla*) and Japanese Larch (*Larix leptolepis*).

Accompanying the introduced trees, some of which have become naturalised, are exotic and often evergreen understorey shrubs, such as Rhododendron (*Rhododendron ponticum*) and Cherry Laurel (*Prunus laurocerasus*), some of which also are now naturalised, their perennial shade suppressing the regeneration of the native deciduous trees and shrubs, and causing decline amongst the vernal herbs that naturally characterise our forests. Where the remaining forest fragments are not suffering from these problems, then naturalised alien herbivores, such as Sika Deer (*Cervus nippon*) and Chinese Muntjac (*Muntiacus reevesi*), often are present, their grazing suppressing the regeneration of the native trees and shrubs.

In the face of all these pressures and the long history of destruction, it comes as no surprise that only tiny fragments of the British Isles are today occupied by forests that resemble at all closely the potential natural forest cover of these islands (Peterken, 1996).

Coda

Attempting to predict the future for the forests of our islands is an almost impossible task, made all the more so by the present uncertainties about future climate changes that may result from human additions of greenhouse gases to the global atmosphere (Houghton, 1997). If greenhouse gas emissions continue, even with the level of abatement agreed at the December 1997 Kyoto Conference of the Parties to the UN Framework Convention on Climate Change, the climate changes that are predicted are sufficient to cause major changes in the potential forest cover of the British Isles. The potential area occupied by forests dominated by broad-leaved, evergreen warm-temperate trees is likely to become much more extensive in southern and western areas, whilst the more Boreal forests of the north will be displaced by forests of temperate, broad-leaved deciduous trees. Forests also will potentially extend to higher elevations in our mountains.

In reality, such potential natural changes will be hindered by the fragmentation of the remaining forest cover, by the impacts of naturalised alien plants and animals, and by human management of the landscape. Given their role as carbon sinks, however, especially in the case of new forests, sequestering carbon released into the atmosphere as fossil fuels are burned, we may see a policy of extensive replanting as part of a response to the problem of 'global warming'. Such replanting is most likely to favour rapidly growing species, however, and may do little to restore our lost native forests or to render our ecosystems more resilient in the face of inevitable climate change. We also will see increased plantation management, including areas of biomass fuel production; here too, however, there are likely to be few benefits to our native forests or their wildlife as fast-growing Willows and Poplars (*Populus* spp.) will be grown as short-cycle coppice.

In short, natural or semi-natural forests already cover only a tiny fraction of the area of the British Isles in the late twentieth century, and their future looks even bleaker.

Acknowledgements

I am grateful to Margaret Atherden, the Director of PLACE, for inviting me to participate in the conference '*Woodland in the Landscape: Past and Future Perspectives*', of which the present volume represents the proceedings. PLACE also provided financial support to enable my participation. Jacqui Huntley read and critically commented upon the first draft of this paper.

References

Behre, K.-E. 1988 The role of man in European vegetation history. *Vegetation History*: Vol. 7 (ed. by Huntley, B. & Webb, T., III), pp. 633-672. Kluwer Academic Publishers, Dordrecht.

Bennett, K.D. 1984 The post-glacial history of *Pinus sylvestris* in the British Isles. *Quaternary Science Reviews* 3, 135-155.

Bennett, K.D. & Birks, H.J.B. 1990 Postglacial history of alder (*Alnus glutinosa* (L.) Gaertn.) in the British Isles. *Journal of Quaternary Science* 5, 123-133.

Birks, H.J.B. 1989 Holocene isochrone maps and patterns of tree-spreading in the British Isles. *Journal of Biogeography* 16, 503-540.

Björkman, L. & Bradshaw, R. 1996 The immigration of *Fagus sylvatica* L. and *Picea abies* (L.) Karst. into a natural forest stand in southern Sweden during the last 2,000 years. *Journal of Biogeography* 23, 235-244.

Bradshaw, R. & Hannon, G. 1992 Climatic change, human influence and disturbance regime in the control of vegetation dynamics within Fiby forest, Sweden. *Journal of Ecology* 80, 625-632.

Chambers, F.M. & Price, S.M. 1985 Palaeoecology of *Alnus* (Alder): Early post-glacial rise in a valley mire, North-West Wales. *New Phytologist* 101, 334-344.

Gear, A.J. & Huntley, B. 1991 Rapid changes in the range limits of Scots Pine 4000 years ago. *Science* 251, 544-547.

Girling, M. 1988 The bark beetle *Scolytus scolytus* (Fabricius) and the possible role of elm disease in the early Neolithic. *Archaeology and the flora of the British Isles* (ed. by Jones, M.), pp. 34-38. Oxford University Committee for Archaeology, Oxford.

Godwin, H. 1975 *The History of the British Flora* 2nd edn, p. 541. Cambridge University Press, Cambridge.

Houghton, J. 1997 *Global warming: the complete briefing* 2nd edn, p. 251. Cambridge University Press, Cambridge.

Huntley, B. 1988 Glacial and Holocene vegetation history: Europe. *Vegetation History* (ed. by Huntley, B. & Webb, T., III), pp. 341-383. Kluwer Academic Publishers, Dordrecht.

Huntley, B. 1990a Dissimilarity mapping between fossil and contemporary pollen spectra in Europe for the past 13,000 years. *Quaternary Research* **33**, 360-376.

Huntley, B. 1990b European vegetation history: Palaeovegetation maps from pollen data - 13,000 yr BP to present. *Journal of Quaternary Science* **5**, 103-122.

Huntley, B. & Birks, H.J.B. 1983 *An atlas of past and present pollen maps for Europe: 0-13,000 B.P.*, p. 667. Cambridge University Press, Cambridge.

Huntley, B., Daniell, J.R.G. & Allen, J.R.M. 1997 Scottish vegetation history: The Highlands. *Botanical Journal of Scotland* **49**, 163-175.

Huntley, B. & Prentice, I.C. 1993 Holocene vegetation and climates of Europe. *Global Climates since the Last Glacial Maximum* (ed. by Wright, H.E., Jr., Kutzbach, J.E., Webb, T., III, Ruddiman, W.F., Street-Perrott, F.A. & Bartlein, P.J.), pp. 136-168. University of Minnesota Press, Minneapolis.

Jones, R.L. & Keen, D.H. 1993 *Pleistocene environments in the British Isles*, p. 346. Chapman & Hall, London.

Mitchell, F. 1976 *The Irish Landscape*, p. 240. Collins, London.

Peterken, G.F. 1996 *Natural Woodland: Ecology and conservation in northern termperate regions*, p. 522. Cambridge University Press, Cambridge.

Wilkins, D.A. 1984 The Flandrian woods of Lewis (Scotland). *Journal of Ecology* **72**, 251-258.

Chapter 2

Wood pasture and the woodland economy in medieval Swaledale

Andrew Fleming

Introduction

Historically there has been a close relationship between wood pasture and rights of common (Rackham, 1976). Given the general history of property and land use rights in the Middle Ages, in many parts of England reading the landscape must involve asking questions about the former existence and whereabouts of wood pasture. This is especially the case in areas like the Pennines, where commons, and rights of common, still exist; the names of each township's moorland commons and daleside cow pastures are frequently marked on maps, and the 'head dykes' which separated them are easily identifiable.

In Swaledale, the northernmost of the Yorkshire Pennine dales, which is the subject of this article, there are patterns of coaxial walls which indicate the whereabouts of formerly subdivided common arable fields and meadows. (Coaxial walls are those which conform to a single axis of orientation and are thus parallel to one another). Field-names of the nineteenth century or earlier confirm the former zonation of land subject to common rights within each township. Many of the closes which now subdivide a former cow pasture had names like 'High Cow Pasture', 'Little Cow Pasture', and so on; subdivided meadows were called 'Great Old Ing', 'Middle Old Ing', etc; names like 'Nelly Bob Dale' or 'William Dale' recall the former existence of 'dales' - coaxially laid out subdivisions of common land. It seems probable that the Swaledale townships, each with its characteristic, easily-identifiable zones of common land, were defined during the last two or three centuries of the Middle Ages. I have argued elsewhere (Fleming, 1998) that as the commons came under increasing pressure, they would have become more closely regulated; at the same time the principles which should have governed the commons were compromised by the creation of intakes. In areas like Swaledale, a major theme of landscape history is the subversion and decline of the medieval communal system of land use. On the map and on the ground, post-medieval intakes and closes are seen to be set within this older framework.

In an article written some time ago (Fleming, 1997), I suggested that in the late Middle Ages each Swaledale township had a largely communal system of land use, which included wood pasture, and that for many townships it is possible to use various lines of evidence and argument to suggest the location of the longest-surviving area of wood pasture. I also argued that the mostly post-medieval pollard elms of central Swaledale represent local survival and continuity of this wood pasture tradition, and that there is evidence for the custom of using leaves for winter fodder - a custom which is also documented in other parts of northern England. In this chapter I will recapitulate the essentials of this argument, before going on to discuss other pollard species and the survival factors which may have affected them. I will then discuss some of the taphonomic and historical issues raised by such work. I will also discuss the relevance of these issues to the genesis and decline of wood pasture in Swaledale.

Wood pasture: working with the evidence
It is worth explaining the different kinds of evidence which may be brought to bear upon the question (Fig. 2.1). The least ambiguous fragment of surviving wood pasture is constituted by a group of alder pollards in what was formerly Ivelet Cow Pasture (which is still largely undivided) at West Arngill Wood (Plate 2.1). There are also single, more scattered pollards, including elm and birch, along this reach of the Swale. Further south in Ivelet Cow Pasture is an intake called 'Mire Plain'.

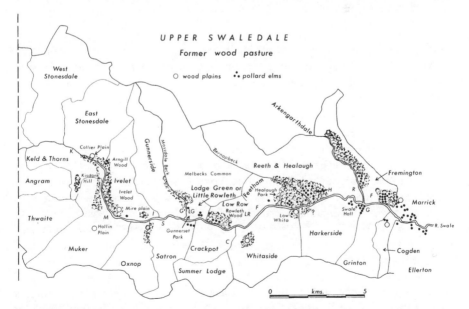

Fig.2.1 General map of Upper Swaledale, mainly to illustrate suggested areas of former wood pasture and the distribution of elm pollards and 'plains'.

Plate 2.1. Alder pollards at West Arngill Wood, Ivelet Pasture.

About a dozen 'plain' names in Swaledale have survived (Fleming 1997: Appendix A). Although in the past two or three centuries these names have usually related to walled closes, I suggest that they originated as the names of open areas or 'lawns' within wood pasture. The name 'Hollin Plain' may indicate a plain where clusters of hollies were maintained as supplies of emergency winter fodder.

Going further east, Great Rowleth Wood, which contains 'stubs' rather than true pollards, still exists as a pastured woodland which is part of Low Row's much attenuated daleside cow pasture; the top edge of the wood gives straight on to the pasture, and the modern road through this wood is unfenced. There are a few elm pollards in the zone between Rowleth Wood and Lodge Green; it will be argued below that zones of elm pollards probably indicate former wood pasture areas.

Across the river from Low Row, the zone around Hollins Farm includes several woodland names, including 'Planes,' ['Plains'] and some fields whose irregular boundaries suggest that they have been won from woodland. There is no evidence here for the coherent outer boundary of 'a wood' - as opposed to a *zone* of woodland. Knowledge of Swaledale surnames over the past three or four centuries suggests that the name 'Hollins' refers here to holly trees, not to a person. Just east of Low Whita (Fig. 2.2) there is a 'plain' name; in the eighteenth century there were

28

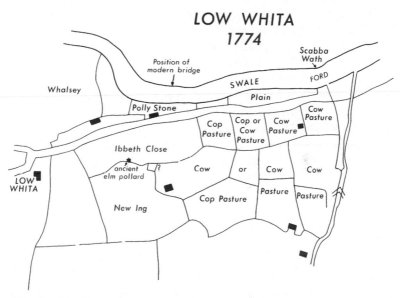

Fig. 2.2 Proposed former wood pasture zone at Low Whita, based on a map of 1774 (NYCRO ZRT 2/3) with field-names supplied from the Grinton Tithe Map (1841).

eleven adjacent fields here with the name 'Cop or Cow Pasture'; 'cop' means pollard in Cumbria (Armstrong *et al.* 1950), and there was until recently a very gnarled, old-looking elm pollard at the top of the field in this area, just above a conspicuous late prehistoric or Romano-British settlement-platform. It may be suggested that this area was formerly a common cow pasture containing pollards.

Just north of Low Whita is Feetham Wood, which is diminutive and situated on a very steep bank just above the Swale. That it carries the township name is significant, and I have suggested that Feetham Wood was once a much larger wood-pasture, taken in by the late medieval Healaugh Park, which lies immediately to the east. Rights of way through the park were preserved. It might be suggested that the same principle operated in Lower Swaledale, and that the parks at Downholme, Marrick and Marske were also taken in from former wood pasture zones. Direct and unambiguous evidence for this is hard to come by, but this may be because these zones had already succumbed to other pressures. For instance, in 1592 the core of Marrick Park was described as 'disuside' and its outer zone was 'newe encloside out of the towne feldes... and convertide from tillage and medowe to pasture' (map in Brotherton Collection, University of Leeds). In Downholme Park, which was licenced in 1377 (VCH, 1914), there is archaeological evidence for a medieval settlement and strip lynchets (T. Laurie, *pers. comm.*). It may be that some outlying wood pasture zones were in land of relatively low value, which was settled relatively late, and could be emparked without much opposition. The practices and management objectives of medieval parks overlapped considerably with those of wood pasture, in the provision of lawns and woodland areas, the harvesting of wood and possibly other woodland products, and also the provision of winter leaf-fodder, for deer and/or cattle. In Swaledale, the woods within Downholme Park contain several elm pollards as well as some old coppice stools, although similar evidence is not apparent in the other parks.

Both Marrick and Downholme have roads leading directly to their respective parks (former wood pastures?), and in some other places it is possible to pick out a potential 'road to the wood pasture'; for example, such lanes lead north out of Muker, and west from Fremington and Healaugh.

Elm pollards

I have also suggested that the wych elm pollards of central Swaledale (Plate 2.2), which are most conspicuous in an area extending roughly from Ellerton to Healaugh, are not to be explained simply or solely as conventional 'boundary' pollards, though many of them *are* on boundaries. Most are now dead, victims of the recent outbreak of Dutch Elm Disease, and some of the dead ones have become victims of the chainsaw. When I arrived on the scene in the mid-1980s, only a few were still to be seen in leaf, and the condition of these has worsened significantly since then. By counting the rings of grown-on stems it is possible to work out that pollarding mostly ceased in the early to mid-nineteenth century, when, according to Rackham (1989), the practice 'went out of fashion'. Local people are largely unaware of the presence or significance of these pollards.

It is possible to check the distribution of the elm pollards against that of major boundary trees in the mid-nineteenth

Plate 2.2 Elm pollard near Healaugh

30

century (which are marked on the superbly-crafted First Edition of the Six Inch Ordnance Survey map, published in 1855). The distribution of major trees did not change very much between 1855 and 1985. In general, elm pollards have only started to disappear in the last fifteen years or so, in the aftermath of disease (eliminating these trees would in any case have been a difficult operation before the advent of the chainsaw). It is clear that the distribution is not random; the elm pollards avoid areas of medieval arable land, notably around Marrick, Fremington, Reeth and Harkerside Place (the medieval township of Herthay or Hercay). Their correlation with suggested areas of former wood pasture is not uniform or absolute. But there are certainly elm pollards, and elm stumps which may represent former pollards, on the western fringes of Healaugh (in the area of the old Thirns Wood, which field names on the tithe map show to have once been extensive) (Fig. 2.3). It is my contention that in Swaledale the pollards largely reflect the post-medieval continuation of tree-lopping practices which were current when wood pasture was common, and that such practices would have been maintained more regularly in areas of former wood pasture than, for example, in former arable fields or meadows. Lopping trees was probably a fairly frequent practice wherever it was a practical proposition and unlikely to result in legal problems.

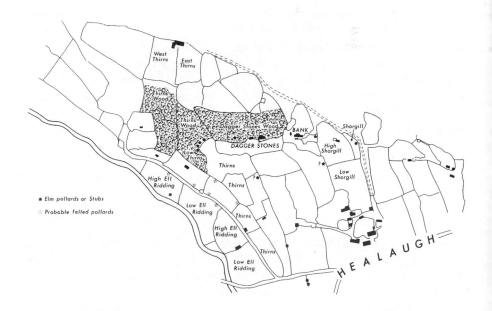

Fig. 2.3 The area west of Healaugh, showing selected early 19th century field-names and the position of pollard elms and some large stumps which may be those of pollards. Note the extensive area covered by 'Thirns' names , and the lane leading from Healaugh to the Thirns area.

The age of the Swaledale elm pollards is somewhat problematic. They are hollow, so direct ring-counting is not possible. I have suggested that a growth rate of $1/2$ inch (13 mm) per annum (or slower) is more likely than a growth rate of $3/4$ inch (19 mm) (Fleming, 1997). On that basis many of the Swaledale elm pollards are about three hundred years old, and a few date from the very late Middle Ages. The very oldest trees will originally have stood beside other pollards, in their youth, in late-surviving wood pasture; but most elm pollards probably represent the continuation of the tree-lopping traditions of wood pasture. Many were undoubtedly planted, mostly on boundaries, and some came to be 'respected' by boundary walls (though loose stones were also put into their crowns and are now held tightly within them). Deliberate planting is obvious in the case of the elm pollards set just inside the precinct wall of the nunnery at Marrick (they were probably planted before the Dissolution), and those which stand along the top of the early medieval earthwork immediately west of Grinton. 'Two Dutch Elms' was planted at Spring End, not far from Gunnerside, to demonstrate allegiance to the royal house of Orange (Pontefract, 1934), though it is not known whether these trees became pollards.

It is also quite likely that a few elms were planted in settlements; 'village elms', on greens and on the street, provided meeting-places, mostly for old men, and they afforded deep shade in the warmer months of the year. There are several nineteenth century references to the presence of these venerable elms in North Yorkshire villages; there was one at Hipswell (just south of Richmond), two in Leyburn, and another just outside the church in Easby. The one in Wensley survived into the middle years of the twentieth century (Speight, 1897; Clarkson, 1821). As their branches became dangerous, such elms would have been lopped, gradually becoming semi-pollards. It is interesting that there is one old elm pollard on what would have been the main axis of what I call 'Old Healaugh', a scatter of house-platforms along the contour above present-day Healaugh. Observation and mid-twentieth century air photographs show that at least two elm trees once grew along the line of the former street of the deserted medieval village at Ellerton - were these descendants of 'village elms'?

Leaf fodder

There are just enough documentary references for Swaledale and neighbouring areas to support the contention that in the Middle Ages trees were pollarded at least in part to obtain leaf fodder. The most striking quotation dates from 1383 and refers to the use of "common between Mosdalbeck [now Gunnerside Beck] and Bernopbeck [Barney Beck] for the whole year for all cattle and animals which the enclosures of Gunnerset Park and Folyng in winter could reasonably sustain, and also to take, cut and pull down branches of trees sufficient within all the woods of Swaledale, as well as for the structure of 'Mosdalhegge', within the bounds aforesaid between Mosdalbeck and Bernopbeck, as for the sustenance of whatever animals and cattle in winter" (Harrison, 1879). The common referred to is Melbecks Common, above Feetham and Low Row, and a group of 'park' field-names on the Tithe Map suggests that 'Gunnersett Park' was in Gunnerside Bottoms, the much-photographed area of walls and field-barns at the intersection of the Swale and Gunnerside Beck (Fleming, 1997). In the early thirteenth century Gilbert de Gaunt's grant to Rievaulx Abbey of a large tract of land in Swaledale included the right to cut evergreen branches for fodder (Fieldhouse and Jennings, 1978). Documents dating from 1618 and 1669 (Ashcroft, 1984) refer to payments made by tenants of the Manor of Muker for *greenhew* (the term used for the privilege of cutting pollards for leaf fodder); the 1618 document refers to the tenants' obligation to "pay their 'greenhewes' as at all tymes heretofore they have usually and accustomably done". Fieldhouse and Jennings (1978) mention a 1726 lease in Walburn which forbade the lopping of trees.

Swaledale may be envisaged as part of a wider area where leaf-foddering was common in the Middle Ages and survived later in some places; Susan Denyer (1991) has recently documented such practices for Cumbria. At Watendlath, not far from Keswick, standing ash pollards (admittedly preserved and managed partly at the behest of the National Trust) may still be seen, both on and within the 'ring garth' as well as on a stony hillside area immediately outside it, where the spacing of the trees is like that within a mature orchard. It has been established that the elm is by some way the most nutritious of the north-west European trees (Austad, 1988). However, since it has also been calculated that a single cow requires the product of about 72 trees for six months of fodder, assuming a leaf-gathering rotation of one year in four (Rasmussen, 1989) it seems likely that the gathering of leaf fodder was mostly about risk-buffering, mitigating the consequences of a poor hay crop. As well-managed hay meadows increased in numbers and area, the frequency of leaf-foddering would probably have declined, though it may still have been important to maintain one's right to lop trees in case of future emergencies - and to maintain suitable trees for this purpose.

There may have been various 'decadent' uses of pollards in post-medieval centuries; elm does not provide good firewood, but it is well suited as material for wooden water pipes, and one Swaledale informant has claimed that elm was used for the 'prods' or pins used in thatching field-barns, largely before the widespread nineteenth century use of stone slates to roof them.

Pollards: other species
It is more difficult to document ash pollards in Swaledale. This is partly because older ash trees tend to 'self-pollard'; major branches break off to produce 'pseudo-pollards', which may then be 'tidied up' by the judicious use of axe, billhook or saw. A tree with this kind of history is hard to identify as a definite pollard - and

there are quite a few Swaledale cases which are problematic in this sense. Furthermore, ash makes excellent firewood, so that an ash pollard is much more likely than an elm pollard to be cut down and sawn up when it is 'middle-aged', rather than allowed to become really old. We should probably expect varying treatment of different tree species, with corresponding implications for their survival chances.

There are quite good reasons for suggesting that ash pollards would once have been more widespread, particularly at the western end of Upper Swaledale. The need for emergency winter fodder would have been as critical in this area as lower down the dale, if not more so. There are few elms or elm pollards here, and this must be significant, given the arguments advanced above for the staying-power of the elm in the landscape. In the far west of Swaledale, the ash is likely to have been the major pollard species. One of the characteristics of the ash pollards at Watendlath is that they are often planted along the 'ring-garth', the outer boundary-wall of a farm or group of farms. In Swaledale there are a few old ashes, some of them possible pollards, which are found in comparable locations.

As we have seen, fragmentary evidence from Upper Swaledale has shown that alder and birch were also pollarded. There is a possibility that the oak, which occurs occasionally in Lower Swaledale, may also have been pollarded. Leaf fodder from oak is not as good as fodder from the elm, ash or lime, but it is perfectly serviceable and there are records of its use in continental Europe (Rasmussen, 1989) and in Nidderdale (Michelmore, 1981). Old oak pollards are to be found in Nidderdale to this day (R. Muir, *pers. comm.*). In Bilsdale, a narrow valley among the North York Moors, the wood book of the Honour of Helmsley lists numerous oak and ash pollards in the mid-seventeenth century (Ashcroft and Hill, 1980); it is clear from the references to their decayed and ancient state that they were survivors from the Middle Ages. On farms where 'dotterds' or 'dotterells' (pollards) were mentioned they tended to outnumber other (presumably 'standard') timber trees. In one group of twelve farms where pollards are mentioned, there were only 540 timber trees, but 1878 pollards, an average of 156 per farm, which, given their apparently elderly state, suggests the survival of a well-developed late medieval tree management tradition. Like the ash, the oak also provides excellent firewood and timber, and is thus as vulnerable to destruction as the ash. If there were oak pollards in Lower Swaledale, they will be long gone.

Oliver Rackham has identified hawthorn pollards in a zone around 500m north-east of Reeth, and suggested that some of them may be about three hundred years old (*pers. comm.*). The extensive wood to the west of Healaugh was called Thirns Wood; it is likely that it was secondary woodland when it got its name, and possible that it included pollard thorns as well as pollard elms.

The use of holly as winter fodder has been well documented for northern England (Radley, 1961; Spray and Smith, 1977; Spray, 1981) and it is likely to have been used in Swaledale too. In Swaledale there are certainly suspicious occurrences of large clumps of hollies quite close to farms. A wood plain near Muker (SD 906977) was 'Hollin Plain' in 1702 (NYCRO Muker Court Records MIC 144); the name 'Hollins' occurs in a zone of late-surviving woodland (see above), and 'Holling Close' crops up on an early eighteenth century map of Downholme Park not far from the lodge where winter cattle-feeding facilities might be expected (NYCRO ZBO (M) 1/5). A large stool of thick holly stems by the roadside at Eskeleth in Arkengarthdale, Swaledale's major tributary valley, is also suggestive (Plate 2.3)

Plate 2.3 Large holly stool at Eskeleth (Arkengarthdale).

Survivorship and continuity of practice

I will now discuss two interrelated issues: one concerns survivorship (already alluded to above), and the other relates to continuity of practice, across the landscape and over time. Swaledale is not East Anglia; in general we are not dealing with a group of long-lasting woods with clearly-defined earthwork boundaries, sets of documents which demonstrate their management history, and complementary floristic evidence (though in some places work could perhaps be undertaken in this area). It is not clear that wood pastures were always or necessarily well-managed according to a predictable pattern by the commoners who had rights within them. In the abstract, it is possible to argue that many commons must have gone through a 'regulated' stage (Fleming, 1998), but various pressures - which in Swaledale may have included the demand for fuel for lead-smelting and timber for mines - may have subverted the maintenance of the common wood pastures. The landscape archaeologist of the late twentieth century has to cope with the consequences of management histories which may well have been complex, unstable through time, and variable in space - and bedevilled by poor survival conditions, both in the landscape and in the archives. The history of tree management and woodland has to be pieced together opportunistically. In these circumstances, the survival of individual phenomena like the Eskeleth holly stool (Plate 2.3) must assume considerable importance. One might write off such a phenomenon as a local freak. But we have to take issues of taphonomy and representativity seriously; the presence of just one centenarian in a community does not imply that, one hundred years ago, only one person was born there. It may sometimes be important to suspend habitual critical scepticism in favour of an open-minded approach to the vagaries of survival.

It may be useful to consider potential spatial and temporal shifts in patterns of wood pasture utilisation. Sometimes, for instance, groups of pollards may have become irrelevant and vulnerable, so that a wood pasture might become a pastured woodland or an open pasture. As suggested above, given the uses to which their wood might be put, oak or ash pollards might well disappear quite rapidly if leaf-foddering ceased, if the land on which they stood was taken out of the commons, or if commons management became more corrupted or casual. In some places, significant names might be the sole surviving form of evidence. In Swaledale, there are field-names such as Ashes and Ashlands, and wood names such as Elmsland Ellers and Thirns (the 'land' element may sometimes derive from Old Norse *lundr*). It seems quite possible that these names reflect deliberate encouragement or propagation of particular species by human management regimes, and hence perhaps imply a zone of former wood pasture.

Areas of wood pasture, then, may readily have become pastured woodland. They may also have become coppices. There are various 'spring' and 'hagg' names in Swaledale which probably relate mostly to coppice. In Bilsdale in the seventeenth century, haggs were clearly coppices (Ashcroft and Hill, 1980); for 'Green Cliffe Hagge', for instance, it was recorded in the Helmsley Wood Book that "this Coppice hee houldes for noe rent and hath much spoiled the springe with keepinge beasse [presumably beasts] in it". As well as reflecting the synonyms for coppice, this quotation also reflects the conflict between the practice of pasturing woodland and the concept of managing it (in whole or part) as coppice, and perhaps also the difficulties of maintaining fences around young coppice compartments. A comparable document dating from 1584 (Harrison, 1879) concerns a wood to the north-east of Swaledale, in the Ravensworth-Whashton area, which refers to 600 horseloads of "toppes and graynes of oaks, hollies and underwood" (which sounds like the product of pollarding, to some extent at least) and records how "Whashton-lowe-Hagge is utterly despoiled with the cattle of Thomas Wraye, the farmer thereof, in depasturing them".

Changes in the importance of wood pasture have been documented by Gledhill, who has chronicled the changing nature of contentious issues in woodland management in Yorkshire, as represented by later medieval court cases. In Period A, essentially before AD 1200, the number of references to pannage exceeded references to wood pasture, which in turn exceeded references to coppice. In Period B (effectively the thirteenth century), wood pasture references were dominant, while pannage references declined, to be overtaken by coppice references around 1300 before dying out altogether. In Period C, the first half of the fourteenth century, coppice references became more frequent than wood pasture references (Gledhill, 1994).

Wood pasture: origins (?) and decline
It would probably be a mistake, however, to suggest a typological sequence in which the first stage was the piecemeal lopping of trees in 'wildwood', or mature secondary woodland, so that pastured woodland gradually evolved into woodpasture with pollards. Lopping the tall trees of such woodland would have been difficult, dangerous and not very effective. It is possible that young 'underwood' trees would be available for pollarding, and that the slow demise of the taller timber trees would eventually allow such new pollards to come into their own. But how many young 'underwood' trees would be available for pollarding in a well-browsed woodland? An alternative scenario would envisage pollarding being developed in open or semi-open areas near settlements or outlying shielings, saplings destined for lopping being selected, protected, and perhaps even planted - the best fodder producers being favoured within the context of locally-available choice. This might produce something like the 'leaf meadows' of Gotland, in the Baltic Sea, where the trees are interspersed with small, irregular hay-growing areas which are moved from time to time.

Well-managed wood pastures near winter settlements would have provided some readily available firewood, and leaf fodder in emergencies. Such wood pastures should then have been located within or just outside 'winter parks' such as 'Gunnersett Park' (see above). The recurrent Swaledale name 'Winter Ings' may also evoke this kind of scenario (at Gunnersett Park field-names such as Great Park, Little Park, Wood Park and Park Foot are accompanied by the names Winterings Field, High Winter Field and Low Winter Field). Presumably the most important aspect of 'winter parks', whether located beside main settlements or further away from them, was winter fodder storage. One might envisage these parks developing when population densities were low, and collaboration between the households within townships, or local communities, was all-important. And just as winter parks were intended to guarantee the survival of domestic stock, so 'deer parks' may have become necessary for the preservation and management of semi-wild deer. 'Herthay', the 'hedged deer enclosure' which became 'Hercay' and then Harkerside, was in being by the later twelfth century (Clay, 1935). In many areas, deer parks, freshly stocked with fallow deer, represented a concept imposed from outside, by the feudal élite. But in woodland areas like Swaledale, such a concept may have converged with known or established management practice. In this wooded environment, the management of deer and cattle, both woodland animals, probably had similar implications in terms of management strategies, and particularly in terms of the characteristics of 'parks' (see above). The convergence of deer and cattle management in a 'woodland' economy is perhaps most effectively attested in the case of the Forest of Pickering (Turton, 1894-7). Here the winter feeding of deer by foresters is well documented; some people had the right to use the wood which remained after the stripping of leaves, or after the bark had been nibbled off (Turton 1894-7, vol 3: xvii, 1. 111-2); they sometimes used it for making charcoal or even for smoking fish!

The most obvious potential wood pastures which are close to settlements are the Low Whita Cow or Cop Pasture (see above) and Thirns Wood, just west of Healaugh, which would have been very near both to 'Old Healaugh' and the present-day Healaugh (Fig. 2.3). Feetham Wood was not very far from Feetham itself. However, these may be remnants of a relatively 'early' scenario. One could easily imagine wood pastures being developed in zones remote from the core areas of the townships, and winter parks being replaced by the storage facilities of individual family groups. In some townships, especially in middle and lower Swaledale, an expansion of arable land at the core may have been responsible for the early demise of 'home' wood pastures; in others, the same effects may have been produced by an increase in the extent and productivity of hay from the 'ings'. 'Distant' wood pastures such as the one at the north end of Ivelet Cow Pasture may have developed late, in various circumstances. Perhaps sometimes, and in some places, there were well-managed tracts of wood pasture occupying parts of the daleside cow pastures. But in other contexts one might envisage the development of a general practice of tree-lopping on the commons, against a background of declining management control, as the commons ethos weakened and decimated pollards were increasingly to be found in more distant and obscure places. There were numerous and varied demands for the resources available on common land, and rapid decline might well follow a lapse in control. Raine (1881) recorded an early sixteenth century court case relating to Marrick Moor in which the lords of the manor carted away and used for lead smelting 'suche wodde as grewe upon the saide ii parcels of grounde' while the tenants 'hadde brakes and haye' for their sheep and cattle, and carried away the 'brakens, ling and thornes'. There is also a reference to thorns being used partly for fodder, partly for firewood, and partly for lead-smelting. And, as mentioned above, the feeding of deer by foresters in winter may also have resulted in the spread of pollards, perhaps in distinctive groups around 'plains'.

Wood and lead production

It is not clear how far the presence of 'bale hills' for lead-smelting would have hastened the demise of wood pasture, and promoted the development and maintenance of coppice (which may be mentioned in Domesday Book, in relation to both Marrick and Ellerton, as '*silva minuta*.' (Faull and Stinson, 1986). In the early sixteenth century, Leland recorded 'no woodd' in Swaledale, apart from 'nutte trees' (which must surely have been an exaggeration); there was 'litle or no woodde' in Arkengarthdale either. But he also states that the wood for lead-smelting 'is brought owte of the parte of the shire, and owt of Dirhamshir', and that 'the best woodes liyeth be est of Swale and Ure rivers' (Toulmin Smith, 1964). So the bulk of the wood for the furnaces was apparently derived from well-organised commercial coppices to the east and north-east, and arrived on pack-horses (which might otherwise have returned 'empty' from Cleveland and the Lower Tees area) travelling along the 'jagger' tracks which run east and north-east from Swaledale and Arkengarthdale (Raistrick, 1962). Perhaps the presence of populous communities with extensive commons, and possibly also the existence of the Forests of Swaledale and Arkengarthdale, as well as the New Forest, ensured that the development of coppices in Swaledale was always rather limited, and could not satisfy the demands of the lead-smelters, at any rate in the later Middle Ages.

The early Middle Ages

If it is not too difficult to suggest a model for the role of wood pasture at around the time of the Norman Conquest, and to suggest reasons for its slow demise, it is much harder to envisage the woodland of the early Middle Ages. It is unlikely that there was much, if any, 'primary' woodland in Swaledale in the early post-Roman period. There are numerous old field-banks, settlement-platforms and enclosures and house-platforms in central Swaledale, not only on the favoured south-facing 'sun side' of the dale but also on north-facing slopes. In their present form, these represent survivals of what must have been a densely-occupied Roman landscape. In Lower Swaledale, this 'ancient landscape' will have been largely eradicated by the extensive medieval arable lands, although a few ancient settlement sites exist in peripheral areas (*pers. comm*. Tim Laurie, who discovered them). At the western end of Upper Swaledale the evidence for 'ancient' fieldbanks and settlement sites gets sparser the further west one travels; this probably reflects the original settlement density. In central Swaledale it seems that the Romano-British settlements have been set within extensive walled land division systems of coaxial type, which extend on to the moorlands and may date from the middle Iron Age. Given the apparent presence of a sizeable Late Roman population in Upper Swaledale, it is not surprising to find that the three linear earthworks which cross central Swaledale, barring approaches to the valleys of the Swale and the Arkle Beck from the east, can be ascribed to the early post-Roman period (Fleming, 1994). However, it seems likely that there was considerably more woodland in Swaledale at the time of the Norman Conquest than in the late Roman period, given the evidence for the existence of medieval wood pasture, the designation of the area as the Forest of Swaledale, the cluster of place-names in 'hay' (*gehaeg*, a hedged enclosure) which includes the two major south bank townships of Herthay ('deer enclosure') (now Harkerside) and Whithay (Whita), and names involving deer such as Hartlakes and Hardstiles (respectively 'deer playing place' (wallow?) and deer path, from '*heort stig*'). It is hard to avoid the conventional view that the population declined somewhat in the post-Roman period, and that the earlier part of the Middle Ages here must have been characterised by a more 'woodland' economy. Much (all?) of this woodland would have been secondary. It is an interesting question whether the Romano-British field walls (which had cores of small stones revetted by well-built faces) would have carried hedges, and how far hedgerow trees would have been pioneer species in post-Roman woodland regeneration.

Conclusion

The answers to the questions surrounding the origins of wood pasture in Swaledale are inevitably provisional and somewhat speculative. However, this Pennine valley ought to repay further investigation. Given that we know a good deal about the location of settlement and land use zones in the later Middle Ages, it should be possible to undertake problem-oriented pollen analyses on carefully chosen sites. If there was indeed quite a lot of woodland regeneration sometime in the earlier medieval period, it may be possible to use such pollen studies to improve our understanding of the development of the earlier medieval landscape. The study of well-preserved charcoal, in association with bale hills and charcoal-burners' platforms, should also be encouraged.

These rather discursive discussions highlight the need for more comprehensive understandings of what may be termed 'woodland economies' (cf. Göransson, 1986). This is hardly an untouched area, but it does tend to be approached tangentially from different research agendas - the interpretation of pollen diagrams, the writing of local histories and histories of woodland management, the development of models for prehistoric agriculture and woodland clearance, and so on. The relevant literature for the European temperate zone spans several languages, and deals with the prehistoric period as well as the historic. Nevertheless, such enquiries should be well worth pursuing.

Acknowledgements
I acknowledge financial help from the Yorkshire Dales National Park, the University of Sheffield, and a Samuel Locker Award (administered by the University of Birmingham). I also thank the staff of North Yorkshire County Record Office at Northallerton; Oliver Rackham, Tim Laurie, Tom Gledhill, Ros Nichol, Lawrence Barker, Susan Denyer and Bill Godfrey for helpful discussions; and Colin Merrony for the line drawings.

References
Armstrong, A. *et al.* 1950. *The place-names of Cumberland.* Cambridge University Press, Cambridge.
Ashcroft, M. Y. 1984. *Documents relating to the Swaledale estates of Lord Wharton in the sixteenth and seventeenth centuries.* North Yorkshire County Record Office, Northallerton.
Ashcroft, M. Y. and Hill, A. M. (eds.) 1980. *Bilsdale Surveys 1637-1851.* North Yorkshire County Record Office, Northallerton.
Austad, I. 1988. Tree pollarding in western Norway. pp. 11-29 in Birks, H. H. *et al.* (eds.) *The cultural landscape: past, present and future.* Cambridge University Press, Cambridge.
Clarkson, C. 1821. *The history and antiquities of Richmond.* Thomas Bowman, Richmond.
Clay, C. 1935. *Early Yorkshire Charters.* vol IV. Yorkshire Record Society, Leeds.
Denyer, S. 1991. *Traditional buildings and life in the Lake District.* Victor Gollancz/Peter Crawley, London.
Faull, M. and Stinson, M. (eds). 1986. *Domesday Book: Yorkshire.* Phillimore, Chichester.
Fieldhouse, R. and Jennings, B. 1978. *A history of Richmond and Swaledale.* Phillimore, Chichester.
Fleming, A. 1994. Swadal, Swar (and Erechwydd?); early medieval polities in Upper Swaledale. *Landscape History* **16**: 17-30.
Fleming, A. 1997. Towards a history of wood-pasture in Swaledale (North Yorkshire). *Landscape History* **19**: 31-47.
Fleming, A. 1998. The changing commons: the case of Swaledale (England) in Gilman, A. and Hunt, R. (eds.) *Property in the Economy.*
Gledhill, T. 1994. *A woodland history of North Yorkshire* (unpublished PhD thesis, University of Sheffield).
Göransson, H. 1986. Man and the forests of nemoral broad-leaved trees during the Stone Age. *Striae* **24**: 145-52.
Harrison, G. 1879. *The history of Yorkshire.* volume 1: Wapentake of Gilling West. Hazell, Watson and Viney, London.

Hicks, S. P. 1972. The impact of man on the East Moor of Derbyshire from Mesolithic times. *Archaeological Journal* **129**: 1-21.

Michelmore, D. J. H. 1981. *The Fountains Abbey Lease Book*. Yorkshire Archaeological Society, Leeds.

Pontefract, E. 1934. *Swaledale*. Dent, London.

Rackham, O. 1976. *Trees and woodland in the British landscape*. Dent, London.

Rackham, O. 1989. *The last forest; the story of Hatfield Forest*. Dent, London.

Radley, J. 1961. Holly as a winter feed *Agricultural History Review* **9**: 89-92.

Raine, J. 1881. Marske, in Swaledale. *Yorkshire Archaeological Journal*. **6**: 172-286.

Raistrick, A. 1962. *Green Tracks in the Pennines*. Dalesman Publishing Co., Clapham.

Rasmussen, P. 1989. Leaf foddering in the earliest neolithic agriculture: evidence from Switzerland and Denmark. *Acta Archaeologica* **60**: 71-86.

Speight, H. 1897. *Romantic Richmondshire*. Elliott Stock, London.

Spray, M. 1981. Holly as a fodder in England. *Agricultural History Review* **29**: 97-110.

Spray, M. and Smith, D. J. 1977. The rise and fall of holly in the Sheffield region. *Transactions of the Hunter Society* **10**: 239-51.

Toulmin Smith, L. (ed.) 1964. *Leland's Itinerary in England and Wales*. Clarendon Press, Oxford.

Turton, R. B. (ed.). 1894-7. *The Honor and Forest of Pickering*. North Riding Record Society, London.

VCH 1914. *Yorkshire North Riding*, vol. 1. Constable, London.

Chapter 3

Judging Woodland Management by Tradition or by Results

Keith Kirby

Introduction

Nature conservation and the maintenance of biodiversity are now amongst the objectives for woodland management, both at a national policy level and, to varying degrees, in each woodland in Britain (HMSO, 1994). This improvement on the situation in the late 1970s and early 1980s follows changes in forestry policies towards ancient and broadleaved woodland and in the training given to professional foresters, the strengthening of site protection mechanisms and an increase in the range of organisations providing advice on woodland conservation (Peterken, 1996; Thomas et al., 1997).

A potent force in bringing about this change was the concept of the 'traditional management' of ancient woodland over centuries, particularly as coppice or coppice-with-standards. This was contrasted with the way such sites were being transformed through clear-felling and planting with conifers under the then-current forestry practices (Peterken, 1977, 1993; Rackham, 1976, 1980). Restoration of coppice was (and is) also widely promoted for woods that have been largely neglected this century to reverse the decline in species, such as woodland butterflies, that thrive under open or young growth stages in the forestry cycle (Warren & Key, 1991).

In the last 20 years, however, continuing research in woodland conservation has developed our ideas, particularly with respect to the role of grazing animals in semi-natural woodland, the importance of dead wood and old trees, and the value of minimum intervention areas as sites where natural disturbance processes operate (Kirby et al., 1994, 1995; Kirby, Reid, Thomas & Goldsmith, 1998; Kirby & Drake, 1993; Peterken & Jones,1987; Peterken, 1996). There have also been advances in our understanding of woodland history (Kirby & Watkins, 1998; other papers this volume).

The principle of using traditional management as a guide to modern nature conservation management is still useful, but is it always applied in the right ways in the light of this new research and the continuing difficulties of funding coppice and wood-pasture systems on a large scale? Should traditional management in the form of restoration of coppice in woods that have had a history of coppice working always be the priority for nature conservation? If it is not, how should decisions be made about what alternative system to adopt; and what surveillance and monitoring is needed to judge the wisdom of such decisions?

Promotion of traditional management as good conservation management
The objectives for woodland nature conservation in England (Kirby, 1993a) are broadly:

> to promote the relatively natural species assemblages and features found in our woodland, particularly those found in ancient semi-natural woodland;

> to maintain populations of rare woodland species;

> to promote across their natural range the populations of all native woodland species.

The treatment of ancient woodland is fundamental to meeting the above objectives, because there are many species, assemblages and features that are restricted to or are most abundant within ancient woods (Rackham, 1976; Peterken, 1993). Since many ancient woods were for centuries treated as coppice, there has been a presumption, in some cases backed by direct research and observation, that these species and features need or do best under a coppice system: otherwise they would have been eliminated in the past. Steele and Peterken (1982) proposed therefore a target of 147,000 ha of ancient semi-natural woodland for coppice treatment across Great Britain, compared to the $c.39,000$ ha which was still being worked (but not all in ancient woods) (Evans, 1992). The 147,000 ha represented about half the then estimate for ancient semi-natural woodland and in the early 1980s there was no likelihood that anything like this extent of coppice would or could be restored to active management. It represented a challenge to more commercially-orientated foresters to come up with alternative approaches that might be easier to adopt under current economic and social conditions, but that would still maintain the species assemblages and features for which coppice woods were particularly valued. These include, for example, the spring flowers and butterflies associated with open ground and the songbirds found in dense coppice regrowth. Other support for restoration of coppice woods can be found in Rackham (1976), Peterken (1993), Fuller and Warren (1990) and Warren and Key (1991).

There has been some increase in the area under coppice in the last fifteen years, with, for example, very strong support for cutting hazel coming from Hampshire County Council (Glynn, 1996), but the total area on a regular cycle is probably still less than 45,000 ha. Recent suggestions for an overall target for worked coppice are only 60-70,000 ha in ancient woodland in England (with only very small areas in Scotland and Wales) (Kirby, 1993b). This reduced target reflects in part the difficulties and costs of bringing out-of-cycle woods back into coppice; and recognition that other types of structures and treatments may have equal or greater benefits than coppice working in nature conservation terms. Coppicing has also been criticised as being unnatural and favouring mainly robust disturbance-tolerant species rather than forest interior specialists (Goldsmith 1992; Hambler & Speight, 1995). Therefore to justify expansion of the area that is worked as coppice for nature conservation reasons requires also an awareness of where and why simply applying 'traditional management' may not always work.

Why may 'traditional management' in former coppice woods not produce 'traditional wildlife benefits'?
Rackham (1976, 1980) and Peterken (1993) stress that each ancient wood has a unique history, which is borne out by countless other studies (Kirby & Watkins, 1998; other papers this volume), but 'traditional management' in coppice restoration schemes is often applied in a standardised way. Key features of past systems may be missed that have important implications for wildlife. The woods themselves have changed compared to their composition and structure 100-200 years ago when coppicing was widespread; the surrounding environment and landscape are very different. Finally the species of most concern from a nature conservation point of view may not be favoured by a return to 'traditional management', or there may be potential conflicts between species in terms of their requirements.

What did traditional coppice management include?
At sites such as the Bradfield Woods in Suffolk or Hayley Wood in Cambridgeshire the coppice system seems to have been carried out fairly consistently for hundreds of years (Rackham, 1976). In other woods there seems to have been much more variation in how neighbouring woods on the one estate were treated, or changes in the detailed treatment of woods over time, for example at Bernwood (Oxfordshire), on the Helmsley Estate (North Yorkshire) and among the Coniston Woods (Barker, 1998; Gulliver, 1998; Thomas, 1998). At different times and places particular coppice species were favoured while others were reduced; the density of standards was increased considerably in some woods, while they were cut out of others; rotation lengths could vary from five to more than fifty years. In the Blean in Kent

even the fine twigs left after coppicing were gathered for kindling (D. Maylam, *pers. comm.*) and the same happened probably more generally. In Flanders (perhaps also in Britain?) bramble *Rubus fruticosus* was cut for fuel for the bread ovens (Tack & Hermy, 1998).

Rarely are all aspects of the former treatment of a site known for the last 100-150 years, and, even if they are, they may be significantly different to the wood's treatment in the 200 years before that. When the wildlife response to coppicing is not what was expected perhaps some part of the 'traditional management' restoration is wrong? Commonly too many standards are left in coppice woods leading to only a limited increase in ground flora diversity after cutting and poor coppice regrowth. Dense bramble thickets are also seen as a problem in restored coppice (Mason & Long, 1987; Carmichael, 1995), perhaps because an associated, but now lost, tradition of cutting it for faggots has not been included in the coppice restoration. Where bramble is removed the flora may be richer (Kirby & Woodell, in press). If small branches and twigs are left after coppicing (rather than being removed as gleanings) more nutrients are retained on the site, so soil conditions (and hence the flora) may change as a consequence.

The woods are different from when they were traditionally managed
Most former coppice woods have gone through 40-70 years as high forest this century. Changes to the woodland structure and composition have occurred such that if coppicing is restored the response is not the same as it would have been 100 years ago. In Monks Wood (Cambridgeshire) tall coppice species such as ash (*Fraxinus excelsior*) have grown up to join the former standards in the canopy, and the stool density in the shrub layer has declined with hawthorn (*Crataegus* spp) increasing and hazel (*Corylus avellana*) decreasing in relative abundance (Crampton *et al.*, in press). Where such stands are re-coppiced the gaps in the stool distribution are often filled by birch (*Betula* spp.), so further change in the woodland composition takes place. The canopy may take longer to re-form because the stool density is lower, which leaves more time for competitive species such as bramble and coarse grasses (particularly *Deschampsia cespitosa*, *Calamagrostis epigejos*, *Holcus mollis*) to dominate the vegetation, compared to stands which have vigorous coppice regrowth.

Some of the flora that appears following coppicing comes from the buried soil seed bank and over the 50 years, where there is dense shade and little soil disturbance in neglected coppice woods, many of the seeds lose their viability (Brown & Oosterhuis, 1981; Brown & Warr, 1992). The diversity of the post-cutting ground flora in restored coppice may consequently be reduced. In a similar way, if a wood and those immediately around it have lost the butterflies and other invertebrates formerly associated with the open stages of coppice, then these may not re-appear if coppicing is resumed.

The ground flora of former coppice woods has also been changing because of increases in stock and deer grazing. Stock grazing was part of many coppice systems, but they were meant to be only in the older growth where they would not damage the underwood (eg. Best, 1998). Stock grazing was controlled by well-maintained internal and external boundaries and by herding. From the seventeenth to early twentieth centuries deer numbers were low throughout much of the country. In the last 50 years stock grazing in upland woods has increased and is now largely free-range; deer densities, both of native and non-native species, have increased considerably (Mitchell & Kirby, 1990; Kirby *et al.,* 1994). The ground flora in a coppice restoration project may be very different therefore according to whether or not it has been protected from grazing prior to the start of the restoration (Cooke *et al.,* 1995).

The effects of a changing landscape and environment
Ancient woodland boundaries have often been stable over centuries, at least in the lowlands, but the surrounding land has changed particularly in the last 50 years, with the loss of hedges, wetland, flower-rich hay meadows and lowland heaths (NCC, 1984; Peterken & Allison, 1989). Coppice woods have lost many of their links to the surrounding countryside (Peterken, 1992). Most have become more isolated, but locally, where new woods have been formed by natural regeneration or planting, they have become less isolated (Kirby & Thomas, 1994; Kirby, Reid, Isaac & Thomas, 1998). The consequences for what should be our approach to woodland management are difficult to predict, but two things seem likely (Figure 3.1).

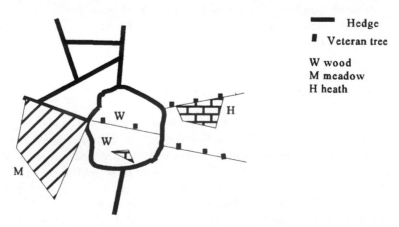

━━━ Hedge
▮ Veteran tree

W wood
M meadow
H heath

Figure 3.1a. Hypothetical nineteenth century landscape. Species A, found mainly in the coppice also relies on the areas of meadow and hedgerow at some stage. Species B, C are found in veteran trees and heathland respectively: while they do occur in the wood their main stronghold is outside it.

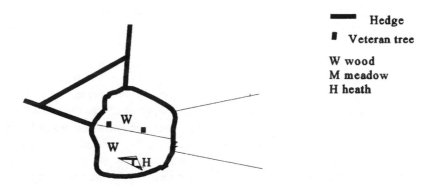

Figure 3.1b. The same landscape in the twentieth century. Species A can no longer occur, even if coppice is restored since the meadow and most hedges are lost. The importance of the woodland for species B and C has increased since their habitats outside the wood have gone.

a. On some sites fewer species will appear in response to restoration (or maintenance) of coppice (so it may be less worth doing) because in the past they also depended on habitats in the surrounding countryside for survival when conditions in the wood itself were not suitable. These habitats around the wood no longer exist, so the source for recolonisation of recently cut coppice is lost. Coppice restoration by itself will not necessarily bring the species back and, even if it does, may not be able to sustain the same population levels of those species as in the past.

b. Some species at the local landscape level now survive only in the woods, even though their main habitat previously was elsewhere. Traditional management should be modified, for example, to reflect the greater significance for nature conservation now of old trees and small areas of grassland within woods, that a century ago might have been more common in the surrounding countryside.

As well as the physical surroundings the environmental context of ancient woodland has changed: woods are subject to greater pollution loads from the atmosphere and from adjacent farmland (Woodin & Farmer, 1993); there may also be effects from changing climate. Some of the violet-feeding butterflies are associated with coppice in Britain because they depend for egg laying and larval development on the warm microclimate created in newly-cut areas, but occur in semi-shaded woods in southern France (Thomas, 1991). Under some future climate-change scenarios their dependence on coppice restoration might be reduced. Increasing soil nitrogen levels have been found in some woods (Farmer, 1995; Thimonier *et al.*, 1992) which favour competitive plant species, particularly if combined with high light levels, rather than those which have more of a stress-tolerant strategy (Grime *et al.*, 1988). To redress the balance more toward the stress-tolerant species, which include many ancient woodland indicators, it may be better not to open up the canopy so much, since it is easier to manipulate light levels than the soil nitrogen levels, ie to shift from coppice more towards a continuous cover type of forestry.

Important species, groups or features may not be favoured by 'traditional management'
Various groups of species may benefit from coppice restoration but for each there may be different recommendations for how restoration is best implemented (Figure 3.2) (Fuller & Warren, 1990; Bright *et al.*, 1996), none of which may correspond to the traditional pattern of cutting on the site. Other important species do not benefit from coppicing at all, for example those that depend on fallen dead wood, continuity of moist micro-climates, or upper canopy conditions (Edwards, 1986; Sterling & Hambler, 1988; Kirby, Reid, Thomas & Goldsmith, 1998). In some cases these species are too poor colonists or their distribution has become too fragmented for them to benefit from the increases in these habitats that have occurred this century under neglect or active conversion of coppice to broadleaved high forest. Others have, however, spread, for example the white admiral (*Limenitis camilla*) and speckled wood (*Pararge aegeria*) butterflies.

The invertebrates of closed canopy broadleaved high forest in Britain are less well-studied than those of coppice woods. Although the former habitat appears extensive and relatively uniform to us it is likely that the associated invertebrates include rare and endangered species that are of as high a priority as those found in worked coppice.

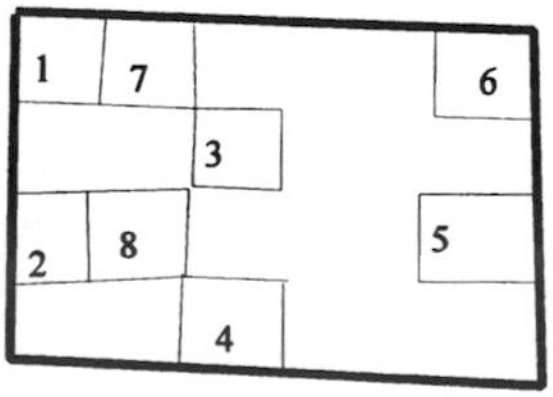

(A)

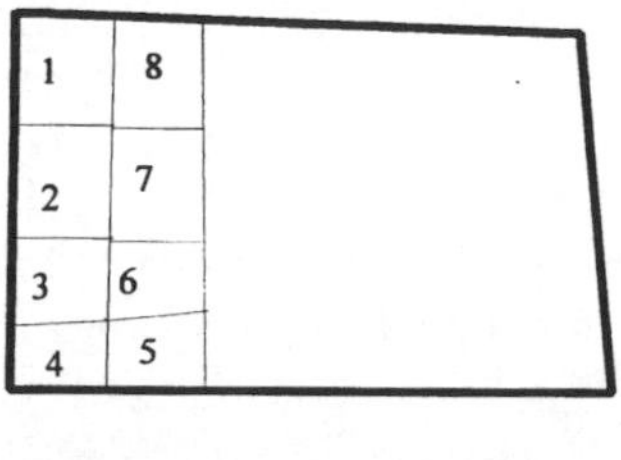

(B)

Figure 3.2. The importance of being clear which species are to be favoured.
(A) shows the recommended layout for coppice coupes to favour dormice. New areas are cut next to old growth to avoid creating large areas all of which are too young to provide much food for the dormice. Ideally coupe size should be small (less than 0.3 ha) (Bright *et al.* 1996). (B) shows the preferred sequence of cutting for butterflies, where the aim is to create large contiguous areas of fairly open stands. Coupes 0.5-1.0 ha are probably best and coupes of less than 0.3 ha are undesirable (Fuller & Warren, 1990).

Features of ancient woodland, such as large old coppice stools and the 'frozen' distributions of different tree and shrub species found in East Anglian woods (Rackham, 1992), are best maintained by coppice restoration. However, in other ancient woods new features and patterns have developed that are of equal importance and that would be lost by a return to traditional management. These include, for example, the pattern of forest dynamics that is developing in Lady Park Wood (Gwent) (formerly coppice, now minimum intervention) as different tree species have gained and lost dominance over the last fifty years (Peterken & Jones, 1987, 1989). Similarly the 1987 and 1990 storms created root plates and pits, natural gaps and horizontal trees, some of which should be recorded and conserved by being left to develop naturally, not cleared to restore traditional management (Buckley *et al.*, 1994).

Moving towards management by desired result not uncertain tradition
English Nature wishes to see a substantial increase in the area of ancient woodland worked as coppice; currently our estimate is that the target should be 60-70,000 ha or about a third of the total area of ancient semi-natural woodland in England (Kirby, 1993b; Kirby & Reid, 1997). This should be concentrated where it will be most beneficial from a nature conservation point of view (Figure 3.3) and there should be preferential support for coppice in such areas, as is happening to a degree through the Forestry Authority's 'Coppice for Butterflies' initiative. Other options provide other nature conservation benefits, for example the increasing amounts of dead wood found in neglected coppice, the larger size of trees and more natural stand dynamics found in high forest systems, the bryophyte carpets of grazed upland woods, the veteran trees of pasture-woodland.

Deciding between options and the detail of how they might be applied should take account of the particular history and current condition of individual sites. Maintaining the coppice cycle in Bradfield Woods (Suffolk) is more critical than at Monks Wood (Cambridgeshire), because in the former the cycle has not been broken, whereas in Monks Wood most of the wood has not been cut for seventy years. Planting of oak may be acceptable in Salcey Forest (Northamptonshire), which was heavily planted with oak in the early nineteenth century, but not in Monks Wood or Bradfield Woods, where there is no record of planting. The current condition and structure of many upland oakwoods is shaped by nearly a century of intensive sheep grazing, but the importance of maintaining some grazing within a particular site will vary from site to site. For example, where there are few gaps in the canopy and a rich ground layer of bryophytes, some grazing is desirable to reduce competition from taller growing ground flora. Regeneration, even if desirable, is likely to be limited by the canopy shade, so there is no advantage from that point of view in reducing grazing. Where there are gaps in the canopy, less bryophyte interest and a need to get some regeneration, then there is a strong case for reducing grazing levels.

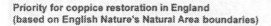

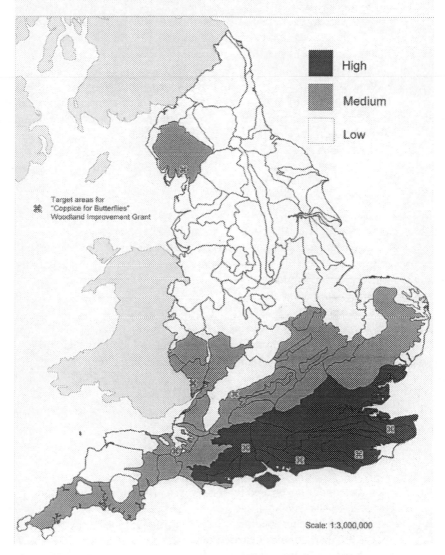

Figure 3.3. Relative priorities for coppice restoration/maintenance across England based on areas with a recent history of coppice cutting, areas likely to show good ground flora or invertebrate responses to coppicing, areas with large old stools and a wide variety of tree and shrub species in the coppice layer. The target areas for the Forestry Authority's 'Coppice for Butterflies' initiative are also shown.

The landscape context of a wood is also important. A coppice cycle can be maintained in very small woods: larger areas are needed to maintain the full range of conditions associated with managed high forest; but in either case the minimum area to make the system economic is likely to be much larger still (Edwards & Kirby, in press). Species populations associated with a particular system (whether coppice or high forest) will be more secure in the long term the larger the area in total being worked in any one year. This is an argument for concentrating on one particular system in any one landscape unit. However, different species will occur in that landscape if some of the woods are managed in a different, complementary way: for instance, if most woods are coppiced then a block that is minimum intervention high forest will probably cater for a very different suite of species (Figure 3.4). The curves in Figure 3.4 are hypothetical; we do not know where the balance lies between encouraging 'more of the same' to promote long-term survival versus management diversity to support current richness. My feeling is that blocks of 50-100 ha should be aimed for where 90% is within one management type and 10% in a subsidiary type; and once this is achieved the balance might switch towards building up a block of woods in which that pattern is reversed.

Management decisions should therefore be assessed both in terms of what is best for the individual site in isolation and, if there is little to choose between options, what will best complement the treatment that is occurring or is likely to occur in the surrounding woods.

Surveillance and monitoring of the success of our management
As management becomes determined less by tradition and more by specific sets of conditions, species, or processes so it becomes increasingly important to assess whether or not these outcomes are achieved.

This may be done at three levels:
a. Are the treatments proposed being undertaken correctly? If the prescription is that the area should be coppiced and this is not done, or if the regrowth fails, eg through deer browsing, then it is unlikely that the desired results will be achieved.

b. Do the conditions created by the prescribed treatments look right; does it appear to the site manager, owner or conservation adviser that the desired species are responding as expected? This is inevitably a subjective process but, particularly if carried out in a structured way, may be all that is required to indicate that the management is working. Frequently it is all that there is time for and it is the principle behind the steps being taken by the nature conservation agencies to the regular monitoring of Sites of Special Scientific Interest (Rowell, 1993).

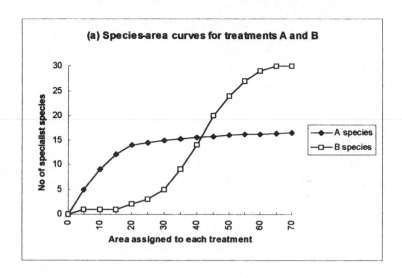

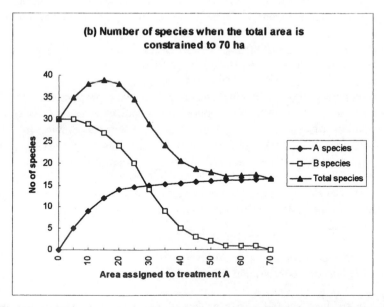

Figure 3.4. (a) Hypothetical species-area curves for specialists associated with either treatment A(coppice) or treatment B(minimum intervention) and (b) the consequences for species number when there is a limited area of woodland available to assign between the two treatments.

The combined species richness peaks when 20 ha out of the 70 ha available are assigned to treatment A, but not all treatment A specialists are present at this level. If it were known that a minimum area of 25 ha for either treatment is needed to sustain populations in the long-term independent of their surroundings then it would be worth increasing the area under A to this minimum even though it would decrease the numbers of B species, and hence the total species number. Any further increase in treatment A would however be undesirable because the total species number declines and, if coppice were increased above 45 ha, then the treatment B (minimum intervention) specialists no longer have sustainable populations.

c. Can we justify, in a quantitative way for a selection of sites, the link between the subjective assessments carried out under (b) and the ultimate nature conservation objectives for which a particular treatment is being proposed? For example, if butterfly populations are observed by the manager to have increased in newly coppiced areas is this likely to be a genuine increase, and is it reasonable to attribute it to the coppice treatment rather than to (say) a general increase in butterflies in all woods?

The work required under (c) involves long-term studies and detailed research that is not practical in most woods. It is, however, essential to separate out different possible causes and types of change. For example, at Monks Wood (Cambridgeshire) T.C.E. Wells believed, from regular observation of the site, that it was becoming more grassy (Wells, 1994). Detailed comparisons between the ground flora in 1990 and maps and quadrat records made in the 1960s and 1970s confirmed that Wells's conclusions were correct (Crampton *et al.,* in press; Cooke *et al.,* 1995). Some small exclosures contained much more bramble (*Rubus fruticosus*) and dog's mercury (*Mercurialis perennis*) than in the surrounding area (Cooke *et al.,* 1995) which suggests that the most likely cause has been the increase in grazing muntjac deer (*Muntiacus reevsii*) and not increased nitrogen deposition, which had been suggested as an alternative explanation.

In Sheephouse Wood (Buckinghamshire) there were proposals to open up the wood. The preferred conservation option was coppice, whereas 2 ha clear-fells with replanting were considered by the owner to be more economic. In the event both treatments were carried out and were assessed using permanent quadrats. Contrary to expectations the clear fells were significantly richer in plant species than the coppice area, but rapidly became dominated by grasses, whereas the coppice area developed dense bramble thickets (Kirby, 1990). However, care must be taken in extrapolating these results to other areas where clear-fell or coppice are being compared:

a. too few standards were removed from the coppice block which probably explains the poor ground flora response initially;

b. in the clear-fell weeds around the planted trees were controlled by mowing between the rows which suppressed bramble and encouraged the grasses.

Had the coppice been opened up more, or another approach been taken to weed control in the clear-fell, the results would have been different.

Conclusions

Traditional management such as coppicing should always be considered when considering how ancient woods should be treated. The area under coppice in England should be substantially increased to about 60-70,000 ha.

Decisions as to where coppice is best restored must allow for changes in our understanding of how woods were managed, how the woods have changed since they were last cut, changes in the environment and their surroundings and in our nature conservation objectives.

Other management techniques are appropriate in some ancient woods, but we need more monitoring of their impacts and research into the dynamics of the woodland flora and fauna that we wish to conserve.

Acknowledgements

My thanks to colleagues in the Nature Conservancy Council and English Nature who helped me with fieldwork and ideas over the years. Thanks also to David Foster and for a Bullard Fellowship at Harvard Forest, where I had the time to speculate on English woodland conservation and management from a distance.

References

Barker, S. 1998. The history of the Coniston woodland, Cumbria, UK. In *The ecological history of European forests,* pp 167-183, edited by K. J. Kirby and C.Watkins, CABI, Wallingford.

Best, J. A. 1998. Persistent outcomes of coppice grazing in Rockingham Forest, Northamptonshire, UK. In *The ecological history of European forests,* pp 63-72, edited by K. J. Kirby and C.Watkins, CABI, Wallingford.

Bright, P., Morris, P. & Mitchell-Jones, A. 1996. *Dormouse conservation handbook.* English Nature, Peterborough.

Brown, A. J. F. & Warr, S. J. 1992. The effects of changing management on seed banks in ancient coppices. In *Ecology and management of coppice woodlands,* edited by G. P. Buckley, pp 147-166, Chapman and Hall, London.

Brown, A. J. F. & Oosterhuis, L. 1981. The role of buried seed in coppicewoods. *Biological Conservation* **21**, 19-38.

Buckley, G. P., Bolas, M. & Kirby, K. J. 1994. Some aspects of treefall-induced soil disturbance of understorey vegetation development following the storm of 1987. In *Ecological responses to the 1987 great storm in the woods of south-east England,* edited by K. J. Kirby & G. P. Buckley, pp 81-104. English Nature (English Nature Science 23), Peterborough.

Carmichael, R. 1995. Woodland bramble: a thorny problem. *Farming and conservation,* **2**, 32-33.

Cooke, A. S., Farrell, L., Kirby, K. J. & Thomas, R. C. 1995. Changes in the abundance and size of dog's mercury apparently associated with grazing by muntjac. *Deer* **9**, 429-433.

Crampton, A. B., Stutter, O., Kirby, K. J. & Welch, R. C. In press. Changes in the composition of Monks Wood National Nature Reserve (Cambridgeshire) 1964-96. *Arboricultural Journal*.

Edwards, K. S. & Kirby, K. J. In press. The potential for developing a normal age structure in managed ancient woodland at a local scale in three English Counties. *Forestry*.

Edwards, M. E. 1986. Disturbance histories of four Snowdonia woodlands and their relations to Atlantic bryophyte distributions. *Biological Conservation* **37**, 301-320.

Evans, J. 1992. Coppice forestry - an overview. In *Ecology and management of coppice woodlands*, edited by G. P. Buckley, pp 18-27, Chapman and Hall, London.

Farmer, A. M. 1995. Soil chemistry change in a lowland English deciduous woodland 1974-1991. *Water, Air and Soil Pollution* **85**, 677-682.

Fuller, R. J. & Warren, M. S. 1990. *Coppiced woodlands: their value for wildlife*. Nature Conservancy Council, Peterborough.

Glynn, L. 1996. The Wessex coppice group: a business development initiative for the hazel coppice industry. *Quarterly Journal of Forestry* **90**, 301-307

Goldsmith, F. B. 1992. Coppicing - a conservation panacea? In *Ecology and management of coppice woodlands*, edited by G. P. Buckley, pp 306-312, Chapman and Hall, London.

Grime, J. P., Hodgson, J. G. & Hunt, R. 1988. *Comparative plant ecology*. Unwin-Hyman, London.

Gulliver, R. 1998. What were woods like in the seventeenth century? Examples from the Helmsley Estate, north-east Yorkshire, UK. In *The ecological history of European forests*, pp 135-153, edited by K. J. Kirby and C.Watkins, CABI, Wallingford.

Hambler, C. & Speight, M. R. 1995. Biodiversity conservation in Britain: science replacing tradition. *British Wildlife* **6**, 137-147.

HMSO 1994. *Sustainable forestry - the UK programme*. HMSO, London.

Kirby, K. J. 1990. Changes in the ground flora of a broadleaved wood within a clear fell, group fells and a coppiced block. *Forestry* **63**, 241-249.

Kirby, K. J. 1993a. Assessing nature conservation values in British woodland - a review of recent practice. *Arboricultural Journal* **17**, 253-276.

Kirby K. J. 1993b. Coppice restoration for nature conservation: how much and where? In *Coppice restoration seminar proceedings*, edited by R. Lightbown & A. Searle, pp 15-24, Institute of Chartered Foresters (Wessex Group) Edinburgh.

Kirby, K. J. & Drake, C. M. (editors) 1993. *Dead wood matters: the ecology and conservation of saproxylic invertebrates in Britain*. English Nature (English Nature Science 7), Peterborough.

Kirby, K. J. & Reid, C. M. 1997. *Preliminary nature conservation objectives for Natural Areas - Woodland and Forestry.* English Nature (Research Report 239), Peterborough.

Kirby, K. J. & Thomas, R. C. 1994. Fragmentation patterns of ancient woodland in England. In *Fragmentation in agricultural landscapes,* edited by J. W. Dover, pp 71-78, Myerscough College (IALE), Preston.

Kirby, K. J. & Watkins, C. 1998. *The ecological history of European forests.* CABI, Wallingford.

Kirby K. J. & Woodell S. R. J. 1998. The distribution and growth of bramble (*Rubus fruticosus*) in British semi-natural woodland and their implications for nature conservation. *Journal of Practical Ecology and Conservation* 2, 31-41.

Kirby, K. J., Mitchell, F. J. & Hester, A. J. 1994. A role for large herbivores (deer and domestic stock) in nature conservation management in British semi-natural woods. *Arboricultural Journal* 18, 381-399.

Kirby, K. J., Reid, C. M., Isaac, D. & Thomas, R. C. 1998. The ancient woodland inventory in England and its uses. In *The ecological history of European forests* pp 323-336, edited by K. J. Kirby and C. Watkins, CABI, Wallingford.

Kirby, K. J., Reid, C. M., Thomas, R. C., & Goldsmith F. B. 1998. Preliminary estimates of fallen dead wood and standing dead trees in managed and unmanaged forests in Britain. *Journal of Applied Ecology* 35, 148-155.

Kirby, K. J., Thomas, R. C., Key, R. S., McLean, I. F. G. & Hodgetts, N. 1995. Pasture woodland and its conservation in Britain. *Biological Journal of the Linnaean Society,* 56 *(suppl.)* 135-153.

Mason, C. & Long, S. 1987. Management of lowland broadleaved woodland, Bovingdon Hall, Essex. In *Conservation monitoring and management,* edited by R. Matthews, pp 37-42, Countryside Commission, Cheltenham.

Mitchell, F. J. G. & Kirby, K. J. 1990. The impact of large herbivores on the conservation of semi-natural woods in the British uplands. *Forestry* 63, 333-354.

NCC 1984. *Nature conservation in Great Britain.* Nature Conservancy Council, Peterborough.

Peterken, G. F. 1977. Habitat conservation priorities in British and European woodlands. *Biological Conservation* 11, 223-236.

Peterken, G. F. 1992. Coppices in the lowland landscape. In *Ecology and management of coppice woodlands,* edited by G. P. Buckley, pp 3-17, Chapman and Hall, London.

Peterken, G. F. 1993. *Woodland conservation and management.* Second edition. Chapman and Hall, London.

Peterken, G. F. 1996. *Natural woodland.* Cambridge University Press, Cambridge.

Peterken, G. F. & Allison, H. 1989. *Trees, woods and hedges: a review of change in the British countryside.* Nature Conservancy Council (Focus on nature conservation 22), Peterborough.

Peterken, G. F. & Jones, E. W. 1987. Forty years of change in Lady Park Wood: the old growth stands. *Journal of Ecology* **75**, 477-512.
Peterken, G. F. & Jones, E. W. 1987. Forty years of change in Lady Park Wood: the young growth stands. *Journal of Ecology* **77**, 401-429.
Rackham, O. 1976. *Trees and woodland in the British landscape.* Dent, London.
Rackham, O. 1980. *Ancient woodland.* Edward Arnold, London.
Rackham, O. 1992. Mixtures, mosaics and clones: the distribution of trees within European woods and forests. In *The ecology of mixed-species stands of trees*, edited by M. G. R. Cannell, D. C. Malcolm & P. A. Robertson, pp 1-20, Blackwell, Oxford.
Rowell, T. 1993. *Common standards for monitoring SSSIs.* Unpublished report, Joint Nature Conservation Committee, Peterborough.
Steele, R. C. & Peterken, G. F. 1982. Management objectives for broadleaved woodland conservation. In *Broadleaves in Britain*, edited by D. C. Malcolm, J. Evans & P. N. Edwards, pp 91-103, Institute of Chartered Foresters, Edinburgh.
Sterling, P. H. & Hambler, C. 1988. Coppicing for conservation: do hazel communities really benefit? In *Woodland conservation and research in the Clay Vale of Oxfordshire and Buckinghamshire*, edited by K. J. Kirby & F. J. Wright, pp 69-80, Nature Conservancy Council, Peterborough.
Tack, G. & Hermy, M. 1998. Historical ecology of woodlands in Flanders. In *The ecological history of European forests*, pp 283-292, edited by K. J. Kirby and C. Watkins, CABI, Wallingford.
Thimonier, A., Dupouey, J. L. & Timbal, J. 1992. Floristic changes in the herb-layer vegetation of a deciduous forest in the Lorraine Plain under the influence of atmospheric deposition. *Forest Ecology and Management* **55**, 149-167.
Thomas, J. A. 1991. Rare species conservation: case studies of European butterflies. In *The scientific management of temperate communities for conservation*, edited by I. F. Spellerberg, F. B. Goldsmith & M. G. Morris, pp 149-198, Blackwell, Oxford.
Thomas, R. C. 1998. Ecological changes in Bernwood Forest - woodland management during the present millennium. In *The ecological history of European forests*, pp 225-239, edited by K. J. Kirby and C. Watkins, CABI, Wallingford.
Thomas, R. C., Kirby, K. J. & Reid, C. M. 1997. The conservation of a fragmented ecosystem within a cultural landscape - the case of ancient woodland in England. *Biological Conservation* **82**, 243-252.
Warren, M. S. & Key, R. S. 1991. Woodlands: past, present and potential for insects. In *The conservation of insects and their habitats*, edited by N. M. Collins & J. A. Thomas, pp 155-211. Academic Press, London.
Wells, T. C. E. 1994. Changes in vegetation and flora. In *Monks Wood National Nature Reserve*, edited by M. E. Massey & R. C. Welch, pp19-28, English Nature, Peterborough.

Woodin, S. J. & Farmer, A. J. 1993. Impacts of sulphur and nitrogen deposition on sites and species of nature conservation importance in Great Britain. *Biological Conservation* **63**, 23-30.

Chapter 4

Woodland Conservation: Past, Present, and Future

Oliver Rackham

What is conservation, and how do we recognize it? The traditional meaning is 'preservation from destructive influences, natural decay, or waste' (*Oxford English Dictionary*, 1st edition). Conservation extends over a vast range of objects, from wildwood and wetlands through cultural landscapes to buildings, pictures and manuscripts. As far as England is concerned, conservation of ecosystems deals with maintaining natural woods, heaths, etc. as part of a cultural landscape.[1]

The classic example of conservation is coppice-woods, which have yielded for century upon century an indefinite supply of produce (Fig. 4.1). The Bradfield Woods in Suffolk (Plate 4.1) have existed in much the same state from some unknown date before 1250 to the present, and as far as we know can continue into the indefinite future (Rackham,1990). Coppice-woods are abundantly documented. One can compare the account of 'boscus de Heyle' in the *Ely Coucher Book* of 1251 with successive descriptions of the wood down the centuries and with Hayley Wood today, a nature reserve of the Cambridgeshire Wildlife Trust (Rackham, 1975). The medieval accounts of Mertonage and Avenells woods in Gamlingay can be compared with the large-scale map of the united wood made in 1601, with the description and map of Gamlingay Wood by R.S. Adamson in 1911 (the earliest ecological account of an English wood), with the earthworks that reveal details too old to appear in written records (Fig. 4.2), and with my own re-survey of the wood, by then also a Cambridgeshire Trust reserve, in 1991 (Rackham, 1992). Within this century thousands of coppices still existed with little alteration since the Middle Ages; if they no longer exist, this is not due to inherent inviability but to changes imposed from outside.

---

[1] In the United States around 1900 there was a debate over the 'conservation' *versus* 'preservation' of American forests, in which 'conservation' was a dirty word, roughly equivalent to 'exploitation' in the bad sense today (Williams, 1989 ch.12; Muir, 1912).

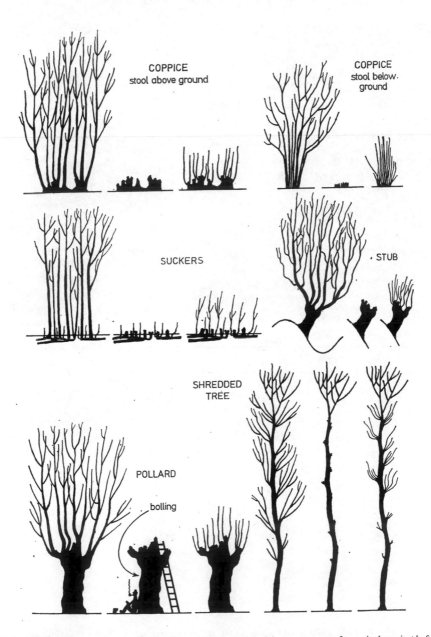

Fig. 4.1. Methods of managing wood-producing trees. For each method the tree, or group of trees, is shown just before cutting, just after cutting, and one year after cutting. All to the same scale. Coppice trees and suckers are to be found in woodland; stubs on woodbanks; pollards in wood-pasture and on wood boundaries; shredding is extinct in Britain but continues in southern Europe. Timber, in contrast, is produced by a separate class of trees left uncut until they reach a size suitable for beams or planks.

Plate 4.1. A coppice-wood in action. Note the scatter of timber trees. *Bradfield Woods, Suffolk, January 1980*

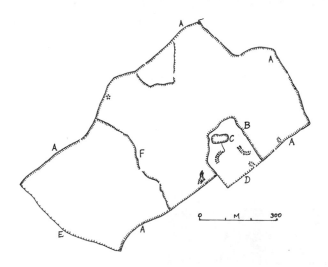

Fig. 4.2. Earthworks of Gamlingay Wood, Cambridgeshire. A: original woodbank, probably of Anglo-Saxon date. B: deviation of original woodbank to exclude some earlier feature, C. D: completion of woodbank after area C had been added to the wood. E: bank corresponding to truncation of wood, probably in the 12th century. F: bank made to define subdivision of wood into Mertonage and Avenells in the 13th century, abandoned in 1601. Although this is perhaps the best documented wood in England, fieldwork reveals features such as B and C that are too early to be recorded in writing

The ancient past
The development of the original natural vegetation of Britain, the *wildwood,* is related by Huntley in Chapter 1 of this volume. Coppicing appears in the archaeological record in the Neolithic period, its produce being used in the hurdlework of the Somerset Levels trackways (Coles & Orme, 1977). At this stage it was evidently intended for growing rods of precise size for particular purposes, and for leaves on which to feed livestock. With most of England still wildwood, conservation is unlikely to have been the main motive.

As the area of woodland shrank in later prehistory, the motive of conservation would have arisen. When wildwood was grubbed out to make fields and pastures, areas that already had a value as coppices were presumably left. The idea of producing specialized material would thus pass naturally into that of conservation; people may not have noticed the transition.

By the Roman period England had a limited area of woodland and a large population, fairly lavish users of domestic and industrial fuel (Rackham, 1980, 1990). Since this state of affairs persisted through several generations of trees we infer that woodland was conserved. The Romans tell us from their writings (e.g. Columella, *Res Rustica* IV.xxxiii.4) that they knew about coppice-woods in Italy, and could calculate the yield. The city of Rome is known to have got most of its wood and timber, unlike its food supplies, from within 200 km (Meiggs, 1982). I calculate that this area would have produced something like 7 tons of timber and wood per head of human population (Grove & Rackham, forthcoming). In England, the Roman iron industry of the Weald produced about 550 tons a year for well over a century, and I calculate that it would have consumed the annual growth of 100 sq.km of coppice-woods (Cleere, 1976; Rackham, 1980 p.108).

The medieval past
It used to be assumed that medieval people rarely indulged in woodland conservation because they did not write about it. In fact the first explicit mention of conservation is by Herbert de Losinga, first Bishop of Norwich, in a letter to his woodward *c*.1100:

As to making a present of Thorpe Wood to the sick or anyone else, I gave you no orders . . . I appointed you the custodian of the wood, not the rooter up of it. To the sick . . . I will give as I did last year, not logs of wood, but money. . . Guard the wood of the Holy Trinity, as you wish to be guarded by the Holy Trinity, and to continue in my favour.[2]

---

[2] Text printed in Supple (1917).

In 1356 the Bishop of Ely was on the run for murder and his lands were seized by the Crown. The king's commissioners reported on:

> a certain Wood called Heylewode which contains 80 acres by estimate. Of the underwood of which there can be sold every year, without causing waste or destruction, 11 acres of underwood which are worth 55*s*. at 5*s*. an acre.[3]

Such explicit allusions to woodland conservation, however, are rare. It was commonplace, taken for granted, and seldom mentioned. Nearly every wood became either a permanent coppice or a formal wood-pasture. When medieval people did mention conservation, there was often a prospect that it would break down. Within 150 years of Herbert de Losinga, Thorpe Wood had lost its trees and turned into Mousehold Heath: it had common-rights of pasture over which the Bishop had no control. (In this century there has been a further failure of conservation: what little remained of the Heath has turned into woodland through lack of grazing.)

The evidence for woodland conservation lies less in documents than on the ground. Ancient woods were valuable, and their conservation depended chiefly on maintaining the boundaries to prevent encroachment and to keep out livestock which would eat the young shoots. Boundary banks (Fig. 4.2) helped with these objectives. At Hindolveston (Norfolk) in 1297–8 Norwich Cathedral Priory constructed banks round both its woods at a cost of £10.10*s*., with more spent on a hedge, bridges, gates, and locks at the entrances (Rackham, 1980 p.158). This followed a switch from timber to wood production, and may reflect the greater importance of security. The massive bank round one of the woods still exists, following all the sinuosities of the wood's outline.

The Hindolveston bank is relatively late; many woodbanks appear to be of Anglo-Saxon date. There is some evidence for Roman woodbanks: occasionally the medieval banks overlie unconformably an earlier, much fainter, system of earthworks (Rackham, 1989a), and in Chalkney Wood (Essex) a long-disused Iron Age holloway is bordered by faint banks. The thousands of man-hours spent on embanking even small woods, and every subdivision of ownership within a wood, attest the importance attached to woodland conservation. Woodbanks ocur widely in Britain, Ireland and France. Even in Essex they were not quite essential: Canfield Hart, although a well-documented medieval wood, preserves its original perimeter with no bank.

I have investigated the fate of the woods of Bury St Edmund's Abbey, one of the greatest landowners of medieval England. The Anglo-Saxon kings, up to 1066 AD, had given the Abbey about 1500 km^2 of land, which included 100-120 km^2 of woodland and wood-pasture in at least 150 separate wood-lots. At least half the

---

[3]   Public Record Office: E143/9/2.

wood-lots disappeared between 1066 and 1250, a time of great pressure on land. These included many of the bigger woods, whose sites turned into pasture commons. The survival rate, however, was much greater for woods within 25 miles of Bury Abbey itself. There is a strong indication that the monks had a woodland policy. Around Bury there was a big demand for wood and timber in the Abbey itself, the town, and the prosperous, woodless Breckland and Fen regions close at hand. Here the monks had embanked and encoppiced some of their woods already before 1086, and the remainder shortly after. Most of these woods survived until the Abbey was dissolved and its lands privatized in 1536; about one-third of them (including the Bradfield Woods) are still there today. They let go the more outlying woods, although any that survived after 1300 were subsequently conserved (Rackham, 1998a).

The inference from this study and from Domesday Book and other documents is that woodland conservation was already important in Anglo-Saxon times but was confined to certain valuable woods, chiefly in parts of the country that had little woodland (Rackham, 1980 ch.9). By 1086 woodland covered 15% of England, but this was still too much for all of it to be conserved. Superfluous woodland continued to be grubbed out and made into farmland, or grazed to an extent that converted it into pasture or heathland, until the fourteenth century, when the population crashed and the pressure on land decreased. Woodland surviving in 1350 – about 6% of England – had a very good chance of surviving the next 500 years.

Wood-pasture

As well as regular woodland, there were areas that combined trees with grazing animals. The distinction between wood-pasture and woodland already existed in Anglo-Saxon times, and is systematically recorded for some counties in Domesday Book. The original wood-pastures were tree'd common-land, in which cattle and sheep grazed between the trees. After the Norman Conquest in 1066 there grew up two other branches of wood-pasture connected with the husbandry of deer (Rackham, 1980 ch.12). The deer might be kept on private land in *parks* surrounded by a deer-proof pale. Or they might be kept in *wooded Forests* by the king or some other very great magnate. In the latter case deer were usually added to the other uses of a wood-pasture common. Like other commons, Forests were of awkward shapes and had no perimeter fence, so that the deer stayed by force of habit. The earliest parks and wooded Forests made use of the native red and roe deer; about 1100 the fallow deer was introduced from southern Europe and rapidly became the principal wood-pasture deer.

In any wood-pasture there is a conflict. The shade of the trees is bad for the pasture, and the livestock eat the regrowth of the trees. Cattle, sheep, and deer are fond of tree leaves, but cannot climb for them, and soon eliminate the supply within reach. Wood-pastures were therefore unlike ordinary woods. The trees might be widely spaced and kept as pollards, cut like coppice stools but at a height at which the animals could not reach the young shoots. This type of wood-pasture belongs to the savanna tradition of land management, with trees widely spaced in grassland, which is still widespread in southern Europe and is not sharply distinguished from the savannas of other continents (Rackham, 1998b; Grove & Rackham, forthcoming). Alternatively, the wood-pasture might be divided into compartments, felled every so often like an ordinary coppice-wood and then fenced until the regrowth was high enough not to be harmed (Fig. 4.3).

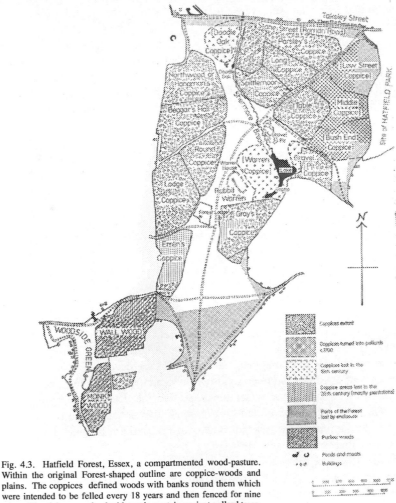

Fig. 4.3. Hatfield Forest, Essex, a compartmented wood-pasture. Within the original Forest-shaped outline are coppice-woods and plains. The coppices defined woods with banks round them which were intended to be felled every 18 years and then fenced for nine years. The plains, grassland with scrub, contain ancient pollard trees.

It has often been claimed that royal Forests preserved woodland. In theory Forest Law forbade the cutting of wood and timber, but there was a tacit understanding that ordinary woodland management was allowed. Forest Law was weakly enforced (Rackham, 1989b). At the start of the Forest system, lands declared to be Forest were not systematically more wooded than the rest of England, and I find no evidence that the survival rate of woods within Forests was greater than for those outside. Any protection given to trees by Forest Law might have been offset by damage due to deer browsing.

On wood-pasture commons, whether Forests or not, trees might be expected to disappear through excessive browsing, as predicted by the theory of the Tragedy of the Commons (Hardin, 1968). Sometimes this happened: early-medieval Thorpe Wood, Norwich, turned into late-medieval Mousehold Heath. The Tragedy of the Commons, however, is a theoretical idea, not based on observing what happened to real commons. Commoners usually got together and agreed on a system of compromises which conserved the trees as well as the other interests. In Hatfield Forest, Essex, there was no Tragedy of the Commons: the compartmented wood-pasture set up in the fourteenth century or earlier had changed very little when the common-rights were abolished in 1857, and is still recognizable today.

Parks, though they normally involved no common-rights, were a troublesome and precarious enterprise, and rarely lasted more than a century or two. The survival of a complete medieval park, such as Staverton Park, E. Suffolk, is a rarity. Since about one-quarter of the woodland in England lay within a park at one time or another, the browsing of deer in parks was a considerable factor in failure to conserve woodland during the Middle Ages.

The modern past
In later centuries woodland conservation was encouraged by the growth of cities and industries as users of charcoal and other products (Plate 4.2). Suppliers of these had a strong interest in maintaining future supplies. Although from the sixteenth century onwards the growing demand for fuel was met mainly from coal, the big concentrations of woodland to survive in England (and Britain) are mainly in areas with big markets for fuel: for example within 60 km of London or 15 km of Canterbury (urban), or The Weald, the southern Lake District, and the Forest of Dean (iron and glass industries). In each of these fuel consumption lasted through many cycles of felling and regrowth of trees.

Changing patterns of use often involved altering the coppice cycle. In the Chilterns, after London took to burning coal instead of wood, the woods and wood-pastures were nearly all converted to the growing of beech as timber (Hepple & Doggett, 1992). From 1780 to 1860 the growth of timber shipbuilding put up the price of oak timber, and encouraged landowners to increase the proportion of timber trees in their woods — except in many oakwood areas, where the even greater

Plate 4.2 A blast furnace, dated 1682. Charcoal was stored in the structure on top. Industrial coppicing was important in the conservation of many well-wooded areas; woodland began to be threatened when the industries ceased. *Guns Mills near the Forest of Dean, October 1993* (shown to me by Dr R. Jarman)

increase in the price of bark for tanning encouraged owners to coppice their oaks and forgo the timber (Rackham, 1980 ch.11).

Nevertheless, the majority of ancient woods survived down to the 1910s with only minor changes, such as lengthening the coppice cycle. 'What period in a site's history ought to be perpetuated?' is not usually now a pressing question for woodland, as it is for some other branches of conservation.

Wood-pastures fared less well. Rarely did they succumb to inherent contradictions or the Tragedy of the Commons; they were more often victims of changes imposed from outside for ideological reasons. In the eighteenth century, throughout Europe, the idea got established that savanna and common-land were bad, and that trees and pasturage should be separated and privatized (Grove & Rackham, forthcoming). In England there was a movement which represented Forests as idle land, seats of indolence, vice, and crime. Its last success was the privatization and destruction of Hainault Forest, Essex in the 1850s. This was a landmark in the history both of the bulldozer and of the modern conservation movement in England, founded to save Epping Forest from a like fate (Rackham, 1978).

Ancient trees, however, were prized as objects of beauty and veneration, and were often preserved as features of landscape parks (Plate 4.3). Even Hatfield Forest survived through being included, for a critical 67 years, within a country-house park. The English affection for ancient trees has led to them being better conserved than elsewhere in Europe.

Although the biological interest of Epping Forest had been recognized, its protection under the Epping Forest Act of 1878 was mainly as a public open space. From the 1920s onwards the idea began that sites of biological interest should be identified and protected as nature reserves. The Bradfield Woods were proposed as a National Nature Reserve in the 1930s, an objective which took sixty years to bring about.

Plate 4.3 Oak savanna of unknown origin, with two generations of ancient trees (the older ones pollarded), conserved by being included in a seventeenth-century landscape park.
Grimsthorpe Park, Lincolnshire, February 1998

When railways came, bringing fossil fuel to remote places, and when the shipbuilding and tanning markets collapsed in the 1860s, woods began to fall into disuse. At the same time continental ideas of modern forestry penetrated England, and it came to be thought that woodland ought to be growing timber, not wood or bark. However, traditions of caution and conservation still prevailed, and well into the twentieth century many woods were still in much the same state as in the Middle Ages. Only in certain areas, such as the Forest of Dean and the South Wales coalfield, was there much attempt to destroy woods and replace them with plantations.

The great onslaught on the woods was delayed until the 1950s, when the ideology prevailed that every inch of available land – even lands which had not been cultivated in the dark and hungry days of the Second World War – ought to appear to be doing something useful. By this time most woods, with exceptions such as the Bradfield Woods, had ceased to be coppiced and were regarded as derelict. From 1950 to 1975 nearly half the remaining ancient woodland was either grubbed out to add to the stock of farmland, or turned over to modern forestry: the trees were felled and poisoned and replaced by planted trees.

The Present

What now remains, thirty-odd years on, are several thousand ancient woods. Those destroyed by agriculture are gone for ever, but the others are in various states:

(1) still coppiced;
(2) disused (or used for shooting or as an amenity) but intact;
(3) damaged by replanting but recovering as the native trees, having recovered from the poison, overtake the planted trees;
(4) replanted but recovering as the site is taken over by self-sown birch and ash;
(5) successfully replanted and unlikely to be recoverable.

The prognosis is now better than at any time this century. Expansion of agriculture is no longer a threat. Encroachments by roads and development are publicly and often successfully resisted. The economic arguments for afforesting woodland have collapsed in ridicule as the planted trees have fallen into neglect or been consumed by drought. (It should have been obvious that the last place for a new plantation is where there are trees already!) In place of the unreformed Forestry Commission, Forest Enterprise has taken a lead in recovering ancient woods damaged by replanting.

Plate 4.4 Oxlip, *Primula elatior,* a plant which (1) is characteristic of ancient woods and does not easily spread; (2) is promoted by coppicing and flowers in profusion in the first year after (as here); (3) is very palatable and damaged by deer. *Hayley Wood, Cambridgeshire, April 1987*

Conservation bodies such as the county wildlife trusts, and later the Woodland Trust, have become major owners of woodland. Ever since the 1960s the object has been not only to prevent woods from being destroyed, but to restore their traditional functioning (Plate 4.4). It was recognized that coppicing was a nearly universal practice of long standing, which had become a necessary part of the environment for many woodland plants and animals.

Woodland conservation fares better than that of any other habitat. In an age when ecology is a political force, ecological science fares less well, but the functioning of woodland is one of the more active areas of research (e.g. Buckley, 1992; Peterken, 1993). One aspect of the change is the publication of English Nature's register of ancient woodland, which is a useful supplement to the system of Sites of Special Scientific Interest. In the context of woodland it is more objective than the SSSI system. Whether or not a given wood is, or is not, ancient has, in principle, a straightforward answer; whereas the question of whether a wood has just enough, or not quite enough, scientific interest to qualify as an SSSI is a difficult and painful decision which is unlikely to be upheld in the light of future increased knowledge.

Wood-pasture fares less well, but there are still a few complete examples (New Forest, Hatfield Forest, Staverton Park) and dozens where parts of the ecosystem, such as ancient trees, survive. A new factor is the recognition that ancient trees (and big dead trees) are not only objects of wonder and delight, but uniquely important habitats in which England is especially rich (Read, 1991). They are not normally to be found in ancient woodland, except in the form of ancient coppice stools.

(Immediately after this paper was read, the WWF published a trenchant critique of English Nature, the official conservation body (WWF-UK, 1997). Almost all the complaints are about non-woodland habitats. Another recent publication reviews the subsequent fate of sites proposed as nature reserves early in the twentieth century (Rothschild & Marren, 1997). It tells a story of destruction and neglect, but seldom in woodland.)

The Future: too much coppicing?
One hears complaints of too much coppicing. There are two lines of argument. Coppicing, it is claimed, is encroaching on the habitat of plants and animals that do not withstand disturbance. Some critics take the stronger line that the only proper objective of conservation is preserving the world's wildwood. If it is answered that Britain cannot do this because there is no wildwood here, we are told that conservationists must drop whatever else they are doing and turn all their energies to *restoring* wildwood (Hambler & Speight, 1995), which in practice means little more than taking existing woods and doing nothing.

Let us put this in perspective. Of the surviving ancient woodland at most 10% is still coppiced or has had coppicing restored. The most strenuous efforts of

Plate 4.5 Giant, presumably ancient stool of jarrah, *Eucalyptus diversicolor,* maintained in coppice-like state by repeated fires.
Avon Valley National Park, Western Australia, December 1986 (shown to me by Mrs J. Mills)

conservationists might conceivably bring this up to 25%. Even this would leave the other 75% mainly for the non-intervention objective. The reply is that 75% is not enough; wildwood restorers think 25% is too much woodland for what is called 'suspect management'.

Restoring wildwood, however, is a nebulous objective. Not enough is known about wildwood in this country to specify in detail what is to be restored. I once foolishly asked whether there were ancient coppice stools in wildwood. The answer is not quite what one would expect. Some North American trees, such as *Castanea dentata* and *Tilia americana,* are self-coppicing and form giant multi-stemmed stools in the nearest approach to wildwood on that continent. The ability to coppice is widespread (but not universal) among the world's trees, including even the unrelated trees of Australia (Plate 4.5); it occurs among palatable and non-palatable, combustible and non-combustible, trees. If we believe in evolution, we can hardly suppose that such an adaptation persisted for millions of years in wildwood without being used.

Much is known of wildwood composition from pollen analysis, and a little about its structure – sizes, ages, and distributions of trees – from 'bog oaks' and other trees preserved in peat. Little is known about herbaceous plants, dead wood,

72

or even whether wildwood was (in modern terms) forest or savanna. Nothing is known about what wildwood would by now have become if any of it had survived. We do know that it will not return merely if existing woods have nothing done to them (Peterken, 1993, 1996). Wildwood, like ancient woodland, was the product of a historic sequence of events which it would be impracticable to repeat. Lime, for example, was the dominant tree in much wildwood, and is still dominant in certain historic woods. But it does not colonize newly-formed woodland, nor increase when woods are abandoned: the conditions for its spread no longer apply. Another irreversible difference from wildwood is introduced animals, of which more later.

Conservation coppicing is nearly aways on sites which have been coppiced in the past, and where any creatures that will not withstand disturbance have (by definition) been banished long ago.

Woods and wood-pastures are part of the cultural landscape. Woodbanks, wood edges, ancient coppice stools, and pollards are part of their historical character and also function as habitats. Woodland conservation is not merely about 'biodiversity' as narrowly defined, but is part of conservation in general; it is wrong (and impolitic) to try to isolate the biological from the cultural components.

The argument against coppicing, however, has its uses. It relieves conservationists of needing to be apologetic about doing nothing. I used to have to defend conservationists who acquired ancient woodland without any immediate plans for 'active' management. In the then prevailing belief that everything in the landscape was no more than the result of human activity, 'neglect' was thought somehow to lead to the deterioration or even disappearance of woodland. Doing nothing has been made a respectable objective; so is trying to re-create wildwood; provided we realize these are two different objectives.

There may come a time when it can properly be said that there is too much coppicing. In my view that time has not yet come; many woodland types are still not well represented in an actively coppiced form. But the point has been reached when the pros and cons of coppicing need to be considered site by site.

Coppicing should not be introduced where it has not happened before. One should not coppice in uncompartmented ancient wood-pasture (but what conservationist would want to?), and probably not in recent woodland, except as an experiment. The longer the time since a wood was last coppiced, the greater the opportunities for species that depend on coppicing to die out, and for species that depend on not coppicing to return (if they can return). Woods known to be rich in plants and animals that coppicing does not favour should not be re-coppiced.

The problem of browsing
The most prevalent counter-indication to coppicing is the practical one of deer. There are now more deer loose in England than for a thousand years. Within 40 km

of Cambridge where I write – perhaps the worst deer terrain in England – there are seven species: two native (red and roe deer), one ancient introduction (fallow), and four modern introductions (muntjac, sika, Chinese water deer, and Père David's deer). Coppicing (and tree-planting) create excellent habitats for deer, which devour coppice shoots, tree seedlings, and the choicer woodland herbs. Woods lived with native deer through the Pleistocene until historic times, but with deer populations constrained either by predators or by the food supply within the wood. In subsequent centuries woods and their ecosystems went on developing without large herbivores, and are very vulnerable when these return. Deer now have no effective predator except the motor-car; they can eat up everything within reach in a wood (Plates 4.6, 4.7) and still have plenty to eat in the fields around.

In this I am pessimistic. Scottish writers to newspapers periodically ask why England cannot have a proper culling programme for deer, as in the Scottish Highlands. But there have been complaints of too many red deer in Scotland for 70 years or more. If it is impossible to control this conspicuous, diurnal, big-game animal which people pay a lot of money to shoot, what hope is there of controlling muntjac around Cambridge?

Plate 4.6 The 'normal' state of a coppice-wood, long uncut, with tree canopy extending to ground level and continuous ground vegetation.
Inside deer-fence, Hayley Wood, June 1980

Plate 4.7 Coppice-wood long uncut and long exposed to fallow deer. Tree canopy ends at an abrupt browse-line 1.24m above ground; ground vegetation is reduced to unpalatable species.
Outside deer-fence, Hayley Wood, May 1984

Conservation and fashion

Conservation, like forestry, is a human activity ruled by fashion: by fashion on a shorter time-scale than the inherent rhythm of the activity. This is illustrated by any long-running nature reserve or national park such as Yellowstone, Epping Forest, Wicken Fen, or Hatfield Forest (Rackham, 1989b). These have been through phases of Do Nothing, Shoot Carnivores, Plant Trees Everywhere, Deny the Site's Cultural History, Be Tidy, Promote Public Access, Destroy Dangerous Trees, and Increase Biodiversity – and now, maybe, Return the Site to Wildwood. Each of these fashions tried to make a site into something that it was not, and subtracted something from the site's real character. Changing the management philosophy every few years can hardly be good for a site. In England there was, maybe, a Coppicing phase which, although more soundly based than most, was occasionally pursued too far in the face of counter-indications.

The matter has deteriorated with the rise of conservation as a profession. Professional conservationists have their own agendas, depending on what was in fashion when they were students; they introduce these fashions to each of the successive sites to which they move. They have careers to pursue and move around quickly; they never acquire that knowledge of sites that comes from years of observation; and too often they do not tolerate opposition from people who do know the sites. Ecological scientists (who belong to a different profession) have a habit of being sacked (or 'made redundant' at the next rationalization) for opening their mouths too wide.

Conservationists are repeating the mistakes of foresters. Half a century ago, official foresters decided that coniferization was 'sound forestry practice' and applied it to nearly all sites, non-woodland or woodland, that they laid hands on. Too late they found out that it was not good practice, even on their own terms. Conservationists risk deciding that so-and-so is 'sound conservation practice', applying it to all the sites that they lay hands on, and finding out too late that it is not good conservation.

Management plans
Management plans were in fashion a few years ago. They were being written for all conservation sites, often by professional (but startlingly inexperienced) writers of management plans. As far as I can discover, most of them went straight into the archives and have never been consulted.

Management plans are supposed to provide continuity: to prevent management from being changed according to the whims of fashion. In practice they fail to do this because they are unreadable and therefore not read, and also because they are supposed to be revised every five years regardless of how long the site has been a reserve. Any new conservation officer, wishing to overthrow the previous management of a site, has merely to do whatever he wants and get it regularized at the next revision.

Management plans should be based on identifying the unique features of a particular site that make it different from other sites. Unfortunately this requires wide knowledge. Professional conservationists tend to ask how a site resembles other sites, and play down its peculiarities. This discourages diversity of sites and management practices. I am surprised that the *National Vegetation Classification* should have become so quickly and widely accepted, despite having too few categories to do justice to the range of variation in British woodland.

Conservation still has to understand its own anthropological aspects, particularly the problem of continuity. Too often proposals are based on the unspoken assumption that the wheel of fashion has at last come to rest and will remain forever stuck at the present day. The conservation movement has a stiff precedent to live up to. Down to this century woods took their chances, and the conservation rate was about 40% in 600 years. Will sites in the hands of conservation bodies fare better?

References

Adamson R. S. 1912 'An ecological study of a Cambridgeshire woodland' *Journal of the Linnaean Society (Botany)* **40**, 339–87, Plates 12–17.

Buckley G. P. 1992 *Ecology & Management of Coppice Woodlands* Chapman & Hall, London.

Cleere H. 1976 'Some operating parameters for Roman ironworks' *Bulletin of the Institute of Archaeology* **13**, 233–46.

Coles J. M. & Orme B. J. 1977 'Neolithic hurdles from Walton Heath, Somerset' *Somerset Levels Papers* **3**, 6–29.

Grove A. T. & Rackham O. (forthcoming) *Ecological History of Southern Europe* [provisional title] Yale University Press.

Hambler C. & Speight M. 1995 'Biodiversity conservation in Britain: science replacing tradition' *British Wildlife* **6**, 137–47.

Hardin G. 1968 'The tragedy of the commons' *Science* **163**, 1243–8.

Hepple L. W. & Doggett A. M. 1992 *The Chilterns* Phillimore, Chichester.

Meiggs R. 1982 *Trees and Timber in the Ancient Mediterranean World* Oxford.

Muir J. 1912 *The Yosemite* Century Co., New York.

Peterken G. 1993 *Woodland Conservation & Management* 2nd ed Chapman & Hall, London.

Peterken G. 1996 *Natural Woodland: ecology and conservation in northern temperate regions* Cambridge.

Rackham O. 1975 *Hayley Wood: its history and ecology* Cambridgeshire & Isle of Ely Naturalists' Trust.

Rackham O. 1978 'Archaeology and land-use history' *Epping Forest – the Natural Aspect?* ed D Corke *Essex Naturalist* **NS 2**, 16–57.

Rackham O. 1980 *Ancient Woodland: its history, vegetation and uses in England* Edward Arnold, London.

Rackham O. 1989a *Ancient Woodland of England: the woods of south-east Essex* Rochford District Council.

Rackham O. 1989b *The Last Forest: the story of Hatfield Forest* Dent, London

Rackham O. 1990 *Trees & Woodland in the British Landscape* 2nd ed Dent, London.

Rackham O. 1992 'Gamlingay Wood' *Nature in Cambridgeshire* **34**, 3–14.

Rackham O. 1998a 'The Abbey Woods' *Bury St Edmunds Abbey* ed A Gransden: British Archaeological Association, forthcoming.

Rackham O. 1998b 'Savanna in Europe' *Ecological History of European Forests* ed K Kirby & C. Watkins: CAB International, Wallingford, forthcoming.

Read H. (ed) 1991 *Pollard and veteran tree management* City of London Corporation.

Rothschild M. & Marren P. 1997 *Rothschild's Reserves: time and fragile nature* Harley, Colchester.

Supple W. R. 1917 *A History of Thorpe-next-Norwich* Norwich.
Williams M. 1989 *The Americans and their Forests* Cambridge.
WWF-UK 1997 *A Muzzled Watchdog? Is English Nature protecting wildlife?*

Chapter 5

The Coal Measure Woodlands of South Yorkshire: Past, Present and Future

Melvyn Jones

Introduction

The solid geology of the exposed Coal Measures of South Yorkshire has had a profound impact on the topography of the area, on patterns of economic development and on the development of the human landscape. The Coal Measures consist of sediments with a characteristic upward sequence of coal, shale, sandstone and seatearth. Following deposition, subsequent faulting, folding, tilting and erosion have given rise to a characteristic 'belted' landscape that rises to 359m in the west and descends to only 19m at the lowest point on its eastern margins. The area is crossed by three major rivers, the Don, Dearne and Rother, the first two having created important gaps through the cuesta system. This topographic variety means that the observer is everywhere aware of the woodlands in the landscape, even though they cover only about 10 per cent of the area. They clothe the scarps and back slopes of the highest edges, and on lower ground they cling to narrow scarps, and hang on steep valley sides right into the heart of the major urban areas.

According to the Nature Conservancy Council's inventory (Eccles, 1986) there were 350 ancient woodlands (including plantations on ancient woodland sites) in South Yorkshire in 1985, of which 290 were on the Coal Measures (Figure 5.1). To these may be added a number of important secondary woods that were planted for aesthetic reasons on country estates or to mask early mining activity, and which in some cases have taken on some of the characteristics of ancient woods (Jones, 1984). In the past all these woods, and others now lost, were managed in four traditional ways: as holts, as holly hags, as wood pastures and as coppices. The evidence for the identification of these woodland sites and the reconstruction of their management histories over the last millennium is plentiful, varied and detailed. The ownership of most of the woodlands by large landed estates such as

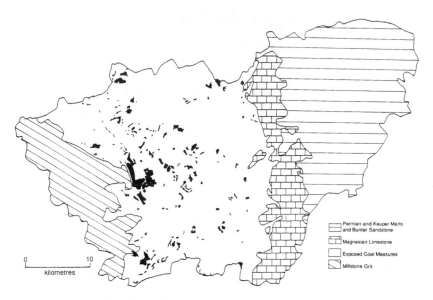

Figure 5.1. Ancient woodlands on the exposed Coal Measures of South Yorkshire, 1985. *Source: Eccles (1986).*

those of the Duke of Norfolk, Earl Fitzwilliam and the Earl of Wharncliffe and their predecessors, means that full and often continuous records over long periods have survived and are accessible in public archives (Jones and Jones, 1985; Jones, 1986a; Jones 1993a). The documentary evidence is often corroborated by landscape archaeology.

This chapter has three complementary aims. Firstly, to chart the evolution of woodland management on the Coal Measures of South Yorkshire, secondly to examine the characteristic features of the main forms of woodland management in the past, and finally to examine the present condition of the surviving woodlands and prospects for their future.

The clearance of the Wildwood
The prehistoric settlers of the Coal Measure country of South Yorkshire have left little direct evidence of their woodland clearance activity, though the finds of stone and metal axes and other implements, hut circles, burial mounds and other earthworks (Latham, 1994), and the increasing number of settlement sites that are being located using aerial photographs (Riley, 1980) all indicate a long occupation of the region that must have been accompanied by much woodland destruction by axe and grazing by domesticated animals.

It was the Anglo-Saxon, Scandinavian and medieval occupants of the region who left behind, through the names they gave to farms, hamlets and villages,

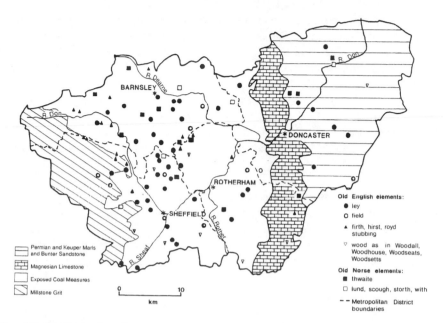

Figure 5.2. Woodland and woodland clearance place-names in South Yorkshire.

widespread evidence of a countryside once covered by and then gradually cleared of woodland. The most widespread of these early place-names are those that mean woodland clearing. Many must indicate large clearings that had existed for many generations before the Anglo-Saxons or Scandinavians entered the region and they were merely renaming them in their own language, but they must have been greatly enlarged and others created as first Saxon and then Scandinavian colonisation took place. Two Old English (Anglo-Saxon) place-name elements that mean clearing which are widespread are *-ley* and *-field*. The *-ley* element helps to make up names like Heeley (high clearing), Longley (long clearing), Hartley (clearing frequented by stags), Totley (clearing of Tota's people), Barnsley (Beorna's clearing), and Norton Lees (clearing at Norton). The *-field* element, which should be interpreted like the Afrikaans *veldt* rather than our modern word field, gives us names like Sheffield (treeless countryside near the River Sheaf), Bradfield (broad stretch of open countryside) and Ecclesfield (open countryside in which stood a British (Celtic) church). The Old Norse (Scandinavian) equivalent of *-field* was *-thwaite* as in Butterthwaite (clearing with rich pasture).

Other significant local early names indicating settlement in a well wooded countryside are *-royd* as in Prior Royd at Ecclesfield, which is Old English and again means clearing, *storth* as in Storrs at Stannington which is Old Norse for wood, and *-lund* as in Lound Side at Chapeltown and Lundwood in Barnsley which is also Old Norse and means a small wood or grove. Names like Woodseats as in Norton Woodseats and Woodhouse as in Wentworth Woodhouse are medieval and indicate offshoot settlements in the woods surrounding the original settlement.

The map showing village, hamlet and farm names (including those now part of the main urban areas) in South Yorkshire indicating woodland and woodland clearing (Figure 5.2) suggests that originally the wildwood was almost continuous in the Lower and Middle Coal Measures, whereas on the Upper Coal Measures, in the Limestone belt and in the fenlands beyond, areas were cleared so early or were never thickly wooded so that woodland and woodland clearance names are far less common.

Woodland at the time of the Domesday survey
Woodland cover had been drastically reduced by the beginning of the Norman period and the countryside was not covered by the boundless wildwood of people's imagination. In many areas what we in the late twentieth century think of as the typical English countryside of hedged or walled fields, winding lanes, isolated farms, hamlets and villages and scattered woods must have been already in existence for centuries.

Oliver Rackham has calculated that the Domesday survey in 1086 covered 27 million acres of land of which 4.1 million were wooded, that is 15 per cent of the surveyed area. His figure for the West Riding of Yorkshire is 16 per cent (Rackham, 1980). My own calculation for South Yorkshire is just under 13 per cent. By way of comparison, woods today, including plantations, cover just over six per cent of the county. On the Coal Measures the figure was 15 per cent at Domesday and just under 10 per cent today. What this means is that in the eleventh century the country generally and the Coal Measure country of South Yorkshire in particular were relatively sparsely wooded even by twentieth-century standards.

Figure 5.3 shows the distribution and types of woodland in South Yorkshire in 1086. With the exception of the giant manor of Hallam, places with woods are shown by circles varying in size according to the extent of the woodland. There are noticeable variations in the distribution of woodland. In the western half of the area, in the Millstone Grit country and on the Coal Measures, woodland was relatively extensive with a substantial number of communities having more than 1000 acres of wood. In contrast, in the Magnesian Limestone belt and the lowlands beyond, the picture was very different. In those areas woodland was more scattered, amounts in individual communities were much smaller than to the west and in nineteen places no woodland was recorded at all. This suggests early clearance and continuous occupation and cultivation by a relatively dense population for thousands of years. The belt of Magnesian Limestone country has long been regarded as the most fertile and attractive area for early settlement in South Yorkshire. This is borne out by the relatively small amount of woodland at

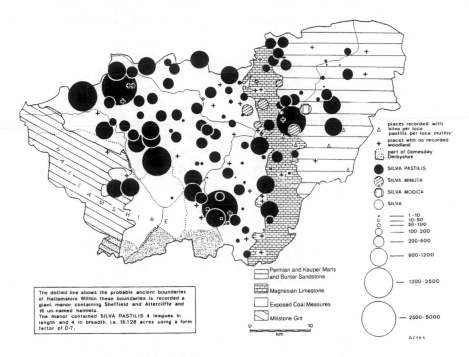

Figure 5.3. Woodland in South Yorkshire at Domesday.
Domesday entries for the West Riding of Yorkshire were given in terms of length and breadth, e.g., Ecclesfield was recorded as containing wood pasture 1 league and a half long and the same wide. The major problem is to convert the Domesday length and breadth measurements into modern areal units. It is generally assumed that a Domesday league was twelve furlongs or a mile and a half. This assumption would give, of course, the dimensions of woodlands that were perfectly square or rectangular, and this was never the case in reality. Moreover, in many cases the linear dimensions must have been arrived at by lumping together two or more woods. To overcome these problems what is called a 'form factor' is used. This is a statistic used to compensate for the oversimplification of the Domesday entries. After comparing Domesday entries with medieval woods of known size which are known not to have changed in the intervening period, Oliver Rackham suggests a form factor of 0.7, i.e., if the length is multiplied by the breadth, it must then be assumed that the woodland area would be about 70 per cent of the figure arrived at. These rules have been applied to construct this map.

Domesday and by the almost total absence of woodland clearance names amongst the villages there.

The types of woodland in South Yorkshire at Domesday also suggest a shortage of woodland in the east of the county and a relative abundance on the Coal Measures. When woods were widespread and populations sparse and scattered they would have been exploited for their trees and also as pastures for cattle, pigs and sheep, i.e., as wood pasture. As populations grew, and demands on the timber increased, and pressure from grazing animals prevented regeneration, woods became scarce and valuable resources and had to be fenced to prevent animals entering them. At the same time a type of management which gave a continuous and self-renewing supply of trees had to be introduced. This was achieved by the more widespread use of coppicing.

Turning to Figure 5.3 again, the key shows that Domesday woodland in the county was described in four different ways: *silva, silva modica, silva minuta* and *silva pastilis*. *Silva* is simply woodland, the meaning of *silva modica* is unclear; *silva minuta* is coppice, and *silva pastilis* is wood pasture. Of the 111 manors in which woodland was recorded in South Yorkshire, seven had coppice woods and 102 had wood pastures. All seven areas of coppice wood were in the eastern half of the county with five in the Magnesian Limestone belt, underlining the view that it was an area of dense population. On the other hand, although wood pasture was found in all parts of the county it was very extensive and the only type of woodland found on the Lower and Middle Coal Measures.

Coppice management from the Middle Ages to the nineteenth century
In the centuries following the Domesday survey, although the wood pasture tradition in South Yorkshire continued to be strong, in the form of wooded commons, deer parks and chases, coppice management gradually became dominant in order to conserve wood supplies which were becoming depleted as the population grew and more and more woodland was cleared for agriculture. Having said that, however, evidence available at the present time suggests that coppice management, which had probably been practised within wood pastures since Neolithic times, did not replace wood pasture on the Coal Measures as the dominant form of woodland management until a comparatively later date.

For example, in a deed dated 1161, the monks of Ecclesfield Priory were given the right to pasture their flocks every year from January to Easter in a large wood on the northern edge of Sheffield, stretching from Birley Edge down to the Don. Beeley Wood and Greno Wood are remnants of this large wood and part of Beeley Wood is still called Priory Wood. The arrangement suggests a wood pasture regime. Nearly 200 years later in 1332, in a document written following the death of Thomas de Furnival, the lord of the Manor of Sheffield, eleven localities were listed under the heading of pastures in woods, moors and commons, including Greno Wood and Beeley Wood, which were originally within the twelfth-century pasture wood described above. Just over 250 years later both of these were coppice woods in which animals were excluded for long periods and were only allowed to graze there under stringently controlled conditions. Other woods are also known to have changed their role from wood pastures to coppice woods during the late medieval period. At least two – Ecclesall Woods and Tinsley Park – were deer parks before becoming compartmented coppice woods.

In the Coal Measure country of South Yorkshire, the form of coppice management called coppice-with-standards had emerged as the most important form of woodland management in economic terms if not in physical extent by the late Middle Ages and continued to be so until at least the middle of the nineteenth century. The underwood in the coppice woods, though predominantly of oak, was mixed (ash, maple, hawthorn, crab apple, elm, alder, birch, hazel, holly, willow, rowan), but the standards were overwhelmingly of oak (*Quercus petraea*), though ash and alder were locally important. When young the timber trees were called wavers (written in South Yorkshire as 'weavers'). When they had grown through two coppice cycles they were referred to locally as 'black barks'. They were then 40-50 years old. Older timber trees were known as 'lordings'. Figure 5.4 shows a typical South Yorkshire Coal Measures wood under a coppice-with-standards management regime.

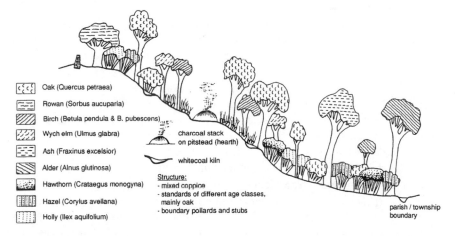

Figure 5.4. Characteristic features of an ancient woodland on the Coal Measures of South Yorkshire under a coppice-with-standards regime.

The earliest-known surviving documentary record of coppice-with-standards management in South Yorkshire is a lease written in Latin at the relatively late date of 1421. The lease concerns a farm at Norton (then part of Derbyshire) and contains a number of clauses concerning charcoal burning and the right to cut underwood and timber. The document refers to the coppices on the farm as *le Spryng bosci* (the spring woods) and to the timber by the usual Latin word of *maerimium*. 'Spring' was the Anglo-Saxon name for a coppice in South Yorkshire.

Two other medieval records of coppice management that mention standards have survived. The first, dated 1462 and written in English, refers to a number of localities in Norton parish thus: ". . . all the wood growing in Rowhawe, Gilleclose, herdyng wood, Whistenhalker, Jackfield, Colynfield and Whitefield . . .". Herdyng Wood is the old name of Rollestone wood which still stands in the middle of a Sheffield housing estate. The document records that John Cotes and John Parker had been granted permission by William Chaworth, knight and lord of Norton, ". . . to fell . . . cole [i.e., to make into charcoal] and carye the said Woddes . . ."preserving for the owner ". . . sufficiaunt Wayvers after the custom of the contre . . .". The mention of wavers, the young timber trees, shows that the woods in question were coppices-with-standards. Wavers are also mentioned in the second document which refers to Hutcliff Wood in the Sheaf Valley at Abbeydale in Sheffield and was written in 1496. The wood at that time was the property of Beauchief Abbey and the document records that " . . . the abbot of Beucheff . . ." had granted permission " . . . to cooll [i.e., to make into charcoal] ii certen woods that is to say hudclyff and the brood medowe Abutt . . .", the woods to be left ". . . weyverd [wavered] workmonlyke . . .".

By the beginning of the seventeenth century coppicing on the Coal Measures of South Yorkshire was entering a golden age. The manor of Sheffield was particularly well wooded. In an undated document written for the 7th Earl of Shrewsbury, the major landowner in Sheffield who succeeded to the title in 1590 and died in 1616, 49 Coal Measure spring woods were listed. In 1637, John Harrison in his 'exact and perfect Survey & View of the Mannor of Sheffield...' (Ronksley, 1908) listed 36 separate spring woods in which the underwood varied in age from four years to 40. Although Harrison did not mention timber trees in the spring woods he named and described, it is clear from other near contemporary documents that the woods on the Arundel estate in Sheffield and Rotherham were coppices-with-standards. The Coal Measure coppice woods supported the local metalworking industries by providing the fuel for iron smelting (charcoal), and lead smelting (whitecoal), and through the provision of building material for the millwrights who built and maintained the many water-powered industrial sites, weirs and river banks (Jones, 1997). The timber and underwood also supported a myriad of local crafts and industries of which leather tanning was the most important (Jones, 1993b). Figure 5.5 shows in some detail the complex web of relationships between woodland management and the wider local economy.

Various aspects of coppice-with-standards management in South Yorkshire are well illustrated in two schemes preserved in the Wentworth Woodhouse archives in Sheffield Archives. These schemes were devised by Thomas Wentworth, 1st Marquis of Rockingham, who inherited the Wentworth estates in 1723. He wrote out in his own hand in 1727 what he called 'A Scheme for making a yearly considerable Profit of Spring Woods in Yorkshire' and in 1749 what he described as 'A Scheme for a Regular Fall of Wood for 21 years...'. In the 1749 scheme a 21-year cycle was used so that the woods coppiced in 1749 would be cut again in 1771. This meant that the Marquis's 876 acres of woodland in South Yorkshire would produce a regular crop of 40 acres of underwood a year for 21 years. Cordwood for charcoal making was the major end use. Two of the woods in the scheme, West Wood and Tinsley Park, were so extensive that they were divided into separate

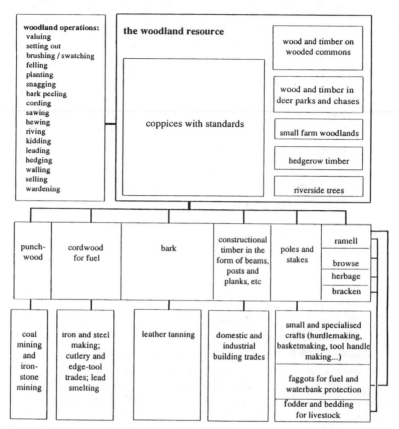

Figure 5.5. Simplified diagrammatic representation of the relationships between woodland management and the wider economy in South Yorkshire in the seventeenth and eighteenth centuries.

compartments that were coppiced at different times. The Marquis was very specific about the timber trees: there were to be five reserves (black barks) and 70 wavers per acre.

The practice of compartmenting large coppice woods is graphically shown in a series of detailed maps produced by the Duke of Norfolk's woodward in 1810. Besides showing the compartments into which the large woods were divided, each map gives the dates of the last fall and the numbers of reserves and wavers preserved in each compartment. One of these maps showing Hall Wood, a well-documented wood of about 70 ha whose boundaries have hardly changed in the last 350 years, is reproduced as Figure 5.6.

One of the features that differentiated coppice woods from other woods was the care and vigilance with which young coppice growth was protected. The

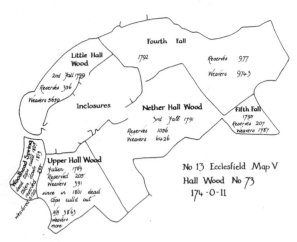

Figure 5.6. Hall Wood as shown on the Duke of Norfolk's woodward's map of 1810. *Source: Arundel Castle Manuscripts She 169.*

proceedings of local manorial courts and woodwards' accounts are full of instances of waiting for and catching offenders, of accusations of theft and trespass, of appearances in court, of fines, and of payments to woodwards' helpers for tracking down suspects and repossessing stolen wood, timber and bark.

From time to time there were eruptions of widespread theft and these led to concerted action. Towards the end of the second decade of the eighteenth century the level of trespass and thefts from the Duke of Norfolk's spring woods was such that Abraham Ibbotson, the Duke's woodward in Sheffield, was granted a warrant by the justices of the peace in 1718 instructing local constables to ". . . make diligent search . . . in the most suspitious houses . . ." and to bring suspects before the magistrates. The constables were spurred on by the phrases "All Excuses & Delays Sett apart" and "Faile not at your perills".

There were particularly sensitive times of the year in the woods. In autumn when berries and nuts were ripe, and in winter, when firewood and food supplies were low, trespass was particularly common. The practice of collecting hazel-nuts in local woods caused widespread damage to wood boundaries and the underwood and prompted the Pegges of Beauchief in 1809 and the Duke of Norfolk in 1812 to post warning notices around their estate and woodland boundaries. The Beauchief notice is shown in Figure 5.7.

Trespass, as a prelude to theft or in the course of taking short cuts was also a common offence. This was accomplished by making gaps in hedges or climbing walls and the damage thus caused, that could lead to animals browsing among the coppice, was of great concern to the woodwards. On 20 May, 1720, Joseph

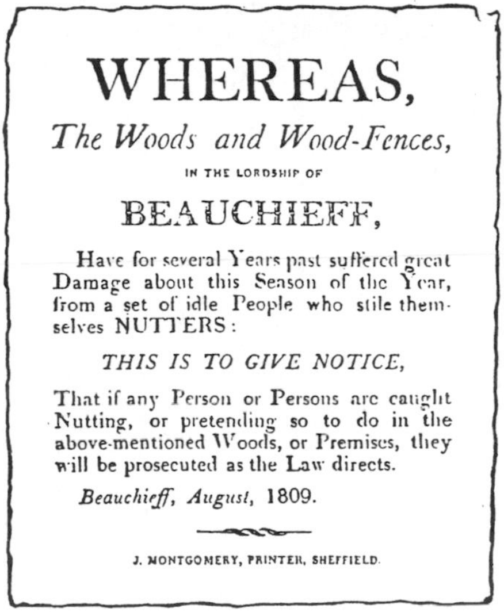

WHEREAS,

The Woods and Wood-Fences,

IN THE LORDSHIP OF

BEAUCHIEFF,

Have for several Years past suffered great Damage about this Season of the Year, from a set of idle People who stile themselves NUTTERS:

THIS IS TO GIVE NOTICE,

That if any Person or Persons are caught Nutting, or pretending so to do in the above-mentioned Woods, or Premises, they will be prosecuted as the Law directs.

Beauchieff, August, 1809.

J. MONTGOMERY, PRINTER, SHEFFIELD.

Figure 5.7. Warning to hazelnut gatherers, Beauchief estate, 1809. *Source: Beauchief Muniments 33-21.*

Shepherd and his wife were paid two shillings for ". . . watching to see who breaks ye Gapp open at ye upper side of Shertley Park (Shirecliffe Park Wood)". The Duke of Norfolk's woodward annotated his entry in the account book to the effect that ". . . M. Bamforth Pull'd it open". Six years later the Duke's woodward paid Richard Wainwright three shillings for waiting for, watching and catching Robert Rawson, a carrier, ". . . who was supposed to break ye old hedge at Shirecliffe Park Wood".

When the coppice was well grown, tenants' animals were allowed access to the woods on payment of a due. For example, Joseph Ashmore, who was woodward to the Duke of Norfolk in the early 1700s, charged himself two shillings in 1710 for "My Mare & fole in Wooley Woods this Spring a month it's old Cutt". This practice was called herbage or agistment.

Sometimes it was necessary to remind the local population that a coppice cycle had just been completed, that the new coppice was at a critical stage in its growth, and that animals should not be allowed to enter the wood. In this connection the vicar of Ecclesfield was paid twopence in 1718 for giving notice to tenants and freeholders, presumably at a Sunday service, to ". . . take care that their cattle do no longer Continue to Graise in Greno Wood for Spoyling ye young sprouts".

In spite of such precautions animals were likely to stray into the coppice woods from neighbouring pastures and commons and this was guarded against by building and keeping in good repair stock-proof fences. These could be in the form of banks and ditches in which the bank was nearest the wood and the ditch was on the outside. The bank was surmounted by a hedge or wall. Such banks and ditches were not as widespread in the Coal Measures of South Yorkshire as in areas further south and east, because of the availability of sandstone from which substantial dry stone walls could be built (see Figure 5.8). There are numerous surviving references to wall repairs around local woods. In July 1719, for example, five wallers were paid £1 13s. 0d. by the Duke of Norfolk's woodward for six days' work ". . . walling down Gapps and low places in Greno Wood fence" and in November 1838 wallers were busy 'gapping' in a large number of woods on the Duke's estate in Sheffield, Ecclesfield and Rotherham.

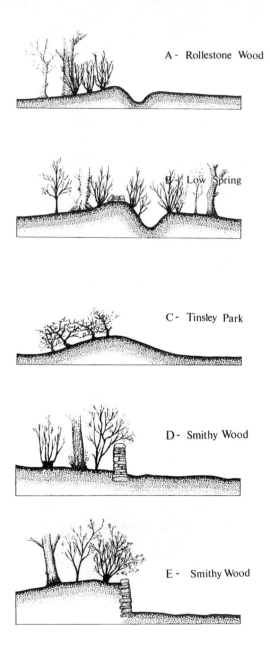

A - Rollestone Wood

B - Low Spring

C - Tinsley Park

D - Smithy Wood

E - Smithy Wood

Figure 5.8. Examples of woodland boundaries on the Coal Measures of South Yorkshire.

Hedgerows were also constantly being replanted around newly felled woods. In 1710 William Sheppard was paid one shilling and eightpence for ". . . hedging 2 days at ye far end of Shertcliffe Park new cutt" and William Walker and his partners were paid £1 19*s*. 8*d*. for completing 136 roods of ". . . spring hedging betwixt Smithy Wood and Jonathan Wingfield's Closes".

Holly hags and holts
Occurring side by side with the coppice wood system throughout the late Middle Ages and into the eighteenth century was the management of holly trees as winter fodder for farm stock, especially sheep, and for deer. The practice was not restricted to South Yorkshire but seems to have been generally associated with upland farming areas in northern England (Spray and Smith, 1977; Spray, 1981). The holly woods, which were either small separate woods or compartments within woods or on wooded commons, were called holly hags. The holly hags were cut on a rotation like other underwood.

The use of holly as winter fodder was recorded in South Yorkshire as early as 1442 when the Lord of Hallamshire's forester at Bradfield noted in his accounts a payment for holly sold for winter feed for livestock. John Harrison, in his survey of the Manor of Sheffield in 1637, recorded 27 separate 'Hollin Hagges' that were rented by farm tenants from the Earl of Arundel.

The custom of using holly as fodder was graphically described in 1725 as a party headed by the Earl of Oxford travelled through Sheffield Park south-eastwards towards Hackenthorpe and Mosbrough. It was noted that they had travelled . . .

through the greatest number of wild stunted holly trees that I ever saw together. They extend themselves on the common...for a considerable way. This tract of ground they grow upon is called the Burley Hollyns...[They have] *their branches lopped off every winter for the support of the sheep which browse upon them, and at the same time are sheltered by the stunted part that is left standing.* (HMC, 29, Portland Manuscripts, VI, 1901).

In the days before the widespread planting of fodder crops for serving to animals in winter, holly and other woody fodder from hedges and woods must have been particularly important in the moorland fringes where stock could not be left to forage for themselves in deep and long lasting snows. In the winter of 1710 the Duke of Norfolk's woodward noted in his accounts that he had paid Henry Bromhead "for him and horse going 2 days in ye great snow to see if any one croped Holling". The impression given was that Pennine fringe farmers were in the habit, in hard winters, of cutting other people's holly. No doubt Bromhead had a blunderbuss over his saddle!

Holly hags also occurred in deer parks. In a lease of Tankersley Park in 1653 it was stipulated that the deer had to be fed by "serving them with holley to be cutt therein in winter" (Hall, 1937). Early nineteenth-century maps of the park show a field called the Far Hollings in the south-east corner of the park and a print of about 1730 shows a small walled wood in that location. Holly is still an important constituent of Bull Wood on the edge of Tankersley Park golf course and this may be the site of another Tankersley Park holly hag. Bull Wood is clearly shown on the 1730 print (see Figure 5.9).

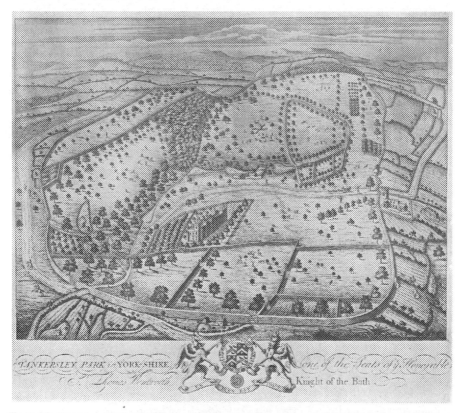

Figure 5.9. Engraving of Tankersley Park in *c*.1730. The two walled woods on the left-hand boundary are holly hags. Bull Wood, a probable, holly hag, is the square-shaped wood on the right-hand boundary beyond the church.

Much less well documented than holly hags were holts. These were what today would be called canopy woods or high forest. In this type of wood maiden trees were allowed to grow to maturity, as were selected poles from coppice stools. Records of such management are restricted to the Wentworth estate in the time of the 2nd Earl of Strafford (d. 1695) and the 1st Marquis of Rockingham (d. 1750).

A deed for 1657 for that estate shows that the 413-acre Tinsley Park was divided into ten coppice woods and three holts. One of these, Old Holt, contained 600 timber trees. Thorncliffe Wood, an ancient wood at Tankersley on the same estate, was said to be 'holted' in a management plan of 1727. Planting took place in such woods and at least one holt on the Wentworth estate was simply a plantation – Hoober Plantation was described as 'a holt on Hoober Hill' in 1723.

Wood pasture survival and decline

As populations grew and settlements and therefore clearance of woodland increased, wood pasture declined and coppice management became predominant. However, wood pasture survived alongside coppices for many centuries. In the medieval period and beyond, wood pastures were found in the Coal Measures country on wooded commons, in deer parks and on chases.

In the Manor of Sheffield in 1637 there were more than 21,000 acres of common, much of it wooded (Ronksley, 1908). Almost all of this disappeared at the time of the Parliamentary Enclosures between 1750-1830 and only fragments remain, one of the largest stretches being Loxley Common, referred to about 1650 as "one Great Wood called Loxley the herbage common and consisteth of great Oake timber". About ten years earlier another wooded common, Walkley Bank, was said to have "a great store of rought Oake trees & some bircke [birch] woods". In the same year another wooded common, Stannington Wood, was said to consist of "pt of rough Timber & pt of Springe wood".

Deer parks, large and small, sometimes well wooded and sometimes only moderately so, studded South Yorkshire in the medieval period (Jones, 1996) as shown in Figure 5.10. Unlike commons, deer parks were areas of private land, bounded by a wall or bank with a cleft-oak paling fence, in which the owner kept deer, hares and rabbits in order to provide his family with a reliable source of meat, and grew timber and underwood. There were more than 200 deer in Tankersley Park in 1653 and 1000 in Sheffield Park in 1637. In the eighteenth century many medieval deer parks were landscaped but often retained their herds of deer, often joined by sheep and cattle. Earl Fitzwilliam even kept buffaloes at one period! Parks contained coppice woods, holly hags and great timber trees. Sheffield Park (its site now covered by housing developments at Park Hill, Norfolk Park, the Manor and Arbourthorne) was famous in its day for the size of its trees. John Evelyn, the seventeenth-century writer, in his book, *Sylva* (1706 edition), described a massive oak tree growing below the Manor which provided 1400 'wairs', which were planks two yards long and one yard wide, and 20 cords (30 tons) of wood from the branches. The local woodward described to Evelyn another oak tree in the park, that was so big that when it was felled and lying on its side, two men on opposite sides of it on horseback could not see each other's hats.

Wood pasture was also a feature of chases, the private equivalent of the Royal

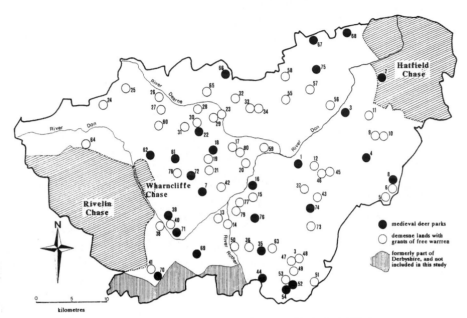

Figure 5.10. Chases, parks and grants of free warren in South Yorkshire in the Middle Ages.

Forests. Chases were areas of land, usually a mixture of heath, moor and woods of various kinds on manorial wastes and unlike parks, chases had no fences and were often intermingled with settlements and farms. There were two chases that were wholly or partly on the Coal Measures of South Yorkshire, Rivelin Chase which belonged to the lords of Hallamshire, and Wharncliffe Chase which belonged to the Wortley family. When Harrison surveyed Rivelin Chase, or Rivelin Firth as he called it, in 1637, he noted within its nearly 7,000 acres an area of particularly stately and ancient trees which occupied the sloping land between Stannington village and the River Rivelin:

> *Item Haw Parke lyeth open to Rivelin ffirth but it is at ye pleasure of ye Lord to Inclose it...This peice is full of excellent Timber of a very great lenght & very Streight & many of them of a great bigness before you come to a Knott in So much that it hath been said by Travellers that they have not seene such Timber in Cristendome.* (Ronksley, 1908, p.152).

Grazing and tree growth do not go well together and on many commons and in parks and chases pollarding was practised in order to produce poles and rods beyond the reach of grazing animals. Two old neglected pollards still survive on Loxley Common.

The extinction of traditional woodland management

The decline of wood pasture management began, as has already been pointed out, in the Middle Ages with the expansion of coppicing, although it was still widespread on wooded commons and in deer parks in the seventeenth century as Harrison's 1637 survey shows. However, it was already in decline.

A substantial part of Sheffield Park was let to tenants by 1637 and eventually the whole park disappeared, first through its sub-division into separate farms, then through the spread of manufacturing and mining activity, and finally through the spread of the built-up area of Sheffield. Now virtually all that is left to remind us of its former presence are place-names and the ruins of the Manor Lodge that stood at the centre of the park. Tankersley Park to the north of Sheffield also went into gradual decline. The hall in the middle of the park was abandoned and subsequently largely dismantled to provide building stone for a farmhouse for a farm that had been carved out of another part of the park. The park was then gradually encroached upon and disfigured by ironstone mining. There was still a herd of deer there in the 1850s even though most of the original park was by then a vast ironstone mining ground. The deer were eventually removed to Wentworth Woodhouse where there is still a herd of about 100 red deer. Other parks in the area were converted in the sixteenth or seventeenth century into coppice woods.

Wood pasture on commons declined steeply in the second half of the eighteenth and the first third of the nineteenth century as commons were enclosed under the Parliamentary Enclosure acts. These 'new' enclosures on old commons are easily recognised by their square and rectangular walled fields as in the case of Stannington Wood (Figure 5.11).

Coppicing itself went into steady decline during the nineteenth century and had virtually disappeared in the Sheffield area by the beginning of the First World War. This decline was partly the result of nationwide changes but there were also important local factors that accelerated its decline in South Yorkshire. The adoption in the eighteenth century by lead smelters, iron makers and some steel makers of coke instead of charcoal and whitecoal meant the loss of major markets. This, coupled with the presence of valuable coal and ironstone seams under many local woods, and the rapid physical growth of Sheffield led to the eventual destruction of centrally located woods and the further contraction of the coppicing tradition. Woods for which records of coppicing stretched back for at least 300 years disappeared under housing and industrial development. The former Burngreave Wood in Sheffield survives only in the form of a few stunted oaks growing over a patch of bluebells in Burngreave Cemetery, and the former 53 acre Hall Carr Wood in Brightside, Sheffield, has left nothing behind but its name. Other nails in the coffin of coppice management locally included the increasing amount of trespass from the growing urban population seeking recreation in the surrounding countryside, which induced the Duke of Norfolk to sell or donate a number of

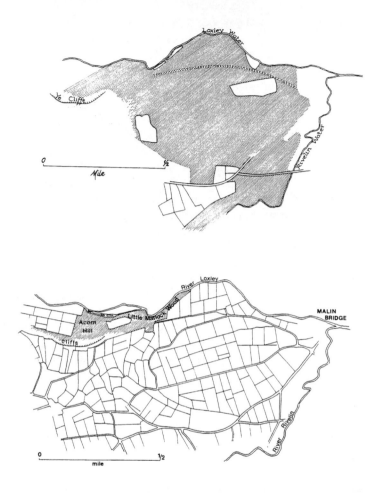

Figure 5.11. Stannington Wood, a wooded common in 1637 (top) and the same site in *c*.1850 (bottom).

woods to local councils. For example, Roe Wood was donated to Sheffield Borough Council by the Duke of Norfolk in 1897 and Wincobank Wood in 1904. Sheffield Council also purchased Bowden Housteads Wood from the Duke in 1914.

By the 1890s coppicing was nearing its end. Income from local coppices had declined sharply and management problems were increasing. As a result more and more woods were gradually converted into canopy woods or 'high forests'. In essence they were becoming plantations, and forestry was replacing woodmanship. This was achieved by singling the multi-stemmed coppice stools in order to allow the best stem to grow into a standard tree, by clearing away altogether the oldest stools and sickly trees, and in their place planting young trees to be grown for timber on a long cycle (Jones and Walker, 1997; Jones, 1998). Many of the newly planted trees were not native to South Yorkshire, trees such as beech, sweet chestnut, common lime and sycamore. Amongst the broadleaved trees, conifers were often planted as a 'nurse crop' for the slower growing broadleaves. For example, in October 1898 the Duke of Norfolk's forester (this title having supplanted the earlier 'woodward') began to systematically plant timber trees in large sections of local coppice woods. In Hesley Wood he planned to plant 100 acres with ash, elm, sycamore, birch, lime, sweet chestnut and beech eight feet apart and 'filled up' at four feet intervals with larch – a total of 145,000 trees. Another 100 acres were to be planted in the same way in Smithy Wood, 120 acres in Greno Wood, 60 acres in Beeley Wood, 40 acres in Bowden Housteads Wood, 25 acres in Hall Wood and 20 acres in Woolley Wood. Conifers were to be planted in all the woods mentioned above, but when he came to Shirecliffe Wood he noted that "being situated nr Sheffield & therefore affected by smoke etc Larch & conifers would not grow well . . .". On 16 November he placed his first order for young trees with a nursery in Cheshire. He ordered, for delivery at Wadsley Bridge Station, 20,000 larch, 10,000 sycamore, 5,000 beech, 2,000 birch and 2,000 sweet chestnut.

Forestry management, including coniferous plantings, has continued to be important right up to the 1990s in some parts of the area and large woods such as Wharncliffe (Forest Enterprise) and Greno (Fountain Forestry) have been almost completely coniferised.

A large number of former coppice woods have come into local authority ownership and are now mostly amenity woods, but since their purchase almost all of them have been managed only on a 'care and maintenance' basis and in consequence they have grown over-mature and their shrub layers have been greatly diminished or have almost disappeared completely.

The future

None of the known late medieval coppice woods on the Coal Measures of South Yorkshire has disappeared through the wanton behaviour of woodmen and other exploiters of wood and timber. Woods have disappeared or have been reduced in size over a long period as a result of the clearance for farmland and mining operations, through the spread of settlement, and through road building. Nevertheless, the survival rate is surprisingly high, a testament to the central importance of woods to the local economy in the past, and more recently to local conservation groups who have assured their survival in the face of heavy pressure from developers. However, with the exception of those still on private estates still managed for timber or for game and those managed by Forest Enterprise, the surviving woods, particularly those owned by the local authorities, have been neglected. By the beginning of the 1980s many of South Yorkshire's surviving Coal Measures ancient woods were even-aged, with dense canopies and poorly developed shrub layers. The more accessible woods were sometimes heavily vandalised.

The benign neglect of the amenity woods made them much less attractive than in the past in that they contained much poorer displays of spring flowers, a significant number of breeding birds and butterflies had been reduced in number or were no longer found in woods where they were once common, and local residents were increasingly afraid of walking in the woods because they were dark and gloomy, and engendered a fear of personal attack. After many centuries of intensive management and careful protection, the twentieth-century attitude seemed, at best, to leave them to their own devices and at worst to abuse them unmercifully or clear them for the sake of progress. Having said that, some ill-judged attempts to re-introduce active management caused much unease, and correspondents to local newspapers criticised what was seen as 'council vandalism'. It became all too clear that managing public woods in heavily populated areas in the late twentieth century was as much about public relations as woodmanship and ecological principles.

During the last two decades there have been some interesting developments. These have been particularly prolific in Sheffield where the City Council has responsibility for more than 60 woodlands, including nearly 40 ancient woods. In the early 1970s the City's Recreation Department created an Amenity Woodland Advisory Group made up of council officers and representatives of environmental organisations (Gilbert, 1982). In 1986 the group commissioned a study to determine the status and management history of the major woods in the City (Jones, 1986b) and this was closely followed by a Woodland Policy document which was approved by the City Council in 1987. In 1991 this was incorporated into the Sheffield Conservation Strategy (Bownes *et al.*, 1991). Meanwhile work had begun in the winter of 1988 on the implementation of a management plan for Bowden Housteads Wood, an important inner city woodland, which had remained unmanaged since its purchase from the Duke of Norfolk in 1914. This was the first example of active woodland management in a non-commercial wood in South Yorkshire in the whole of the twentieth century! Other management plans followed, prepared not only by City Council officers but also by local environmental groups. Most recently, a series of carefully monitored coppicing experiments have been set up in four different woods in the City to assess the ecological and economic impact of the coppiced coupes and to evaluate visitor reaction to the re-introduction of intensive management in well-visited woods (Jones and Talbot, 1995; Rotherham, 1996).

Similar developments have taken place in Rotherham Metropolitan Borough where there are more than 20 ancient woods in public ownership. In 1988 the

Planning Department commissioned detailed studies of all the ancient woods in the Borough. These studies highlighted the historical and ecological significance of the surviving woods and in many cases their neglected state (Jones, 1989-92). A woodland officer has been in post for a number of years and there is now a wider appreciation of the value of the Borough's woodlands and the need to actively manage them. Detailed management plans have been drawn up for half a dozen woods and others are in preparation. Implementation of approved plans is most advanced in Scholes Coppice, which was awarded a Centre of Excellence Award by the Forestry Commission in 1995.

In Barnsley, one of the most exciting projects under the auspices of the Countryside Action in the Rural Environment (CARE) Project, has been the purchase from the Forestry Commission in 1989 by Tankersley Parish Council of Broad Ing Wood, a plantation of sycamore and Japanese larch on an ancient woodland site. The local community, with professional advice, have transformed the site from a close set plantation into an amenity wood with a semi-natural character and carpets of bluebells (Jones, 1988).

A major influence on local attitudes to woodland management in the last few years has been the South Yorkshire Forest Project. This project, established in 1991, is a partnership between Barnsley, Rotherham and Sheffield Councils, the Countryside Commission and the Forestry Commission. Its aim is to 'develop multipurpose forests which will create better environments for people to use, cherish and enjoy'. The South Yorkshire Forest area covers most of the Coal Measures. Although it is not just concerned with ancient woodlands, among its objectives are commitments to protect areas of historical, archaeological and ecological interest (i.e. the existing ancient woodlands), to increase opportunities for access and recreation, and to encourage the development of timber-based industries, employment opportunities and woodland products. Following a year of public consultation, the *South Yorkshire Forest Plan* was published in August 1994. This establishes a policy framework and a strategic approach to woodland management throughout the South Yorkshire Forest area – for private as well as publicly-owned woods – and will guide developments well into the next century. At the time of writing the South Yorkshire Forest Team and their partners await the outcome of a £1½m bid to the Heritage Lottery Fund for a five-year action plan to restore 35 Coal Measure woodlands (South Yorkshire Forest Partnership, 1997).

All these new initiatives involve the re-introduction, in some form or other, and at a variety of scales, of commercial coppicing. If this is to be sustained then old markets for wood and timber will have to be revived and new markets found. There are undoubted opportunities for suppliers of local wood and timber to supply South Yorkshire markets for firewood kindling, rustic poles, log rolls for garden edging, fencing materials, bagged forest bark and mulch material, quality hardwood and barbecue charcoal (Birks, 1995). The market for locally-produced barbecue charcoal in particular is one that is being developed up and down the country. The London Borough of Croydon, for example, has decided to convert the felled wood from its parks and 34 miles of tree-lined streets into charcoal. Sales are expected to be of the value of £50,000 per year. In South Yorkshire four charcoalmakers and one pole lathe turner have set up operations since 1990.

The renewed interest in woodland conservation and management has been marked by an almost universal enthusiasm for the coppicing tradition. There are now, however, some dissenting voices and counsels of caution. Some observers have claimed that too much emphasis has been placed on early successional habitats and on management for the conservation of certain conspicuous and charismatic species such as butterflies and ground flora (Hambler and Speight, 1995). Enthusiasts for conservation coppicing have also counselled greater rationality and more strategic thinking before embarking on re-coppicing schemes (Booker and Tittensor, 1992). Clearly, there needs to be careful monitoring of the ecological, economic, and recreational impact of the new fashion for 'interventionist' woodland management.

In spite of these caveats the future of South Yorkshire's ancient woods looks much better now than it did two decades ago. Awareness of the cultural importance of local ancient woods has been raised to a much higher level than hitherto and interest in their economic as well as recreational potential has been re-awakened. But it must be remembered that woodland management is not a one-off event: it is continuous and long-term. The work that is currently taking place is just the beginning; the challenge is to sustain it in the medium and long term.

References

1. Documentary sources
I am grateful for permission from the copyright owners to consult, quote from and reproduce extracts from the following documents:

Sheffield Archives
Arundel Castle Manuscripts, S 277-292, S 296, S 300, S 301, S 303, S 54, She 169.
Beauchief Muniments, 33-21, 43-46, 994.
Bright Papers, D 365.
Fairbank Collection, She D 300L.
Jackson Collection, 264, 299.
Wentworth Woodhouse Muniments, A 257-485, A 700-44, A 1273, D 365, D 778-782, MP 42, MP 44, MP 46.

Lambeth Palace Library, London
Shrewsbury Papers, MS 698, Vol 3.

2. Books, articles and published and unpublished reports

Birks, C. 1995 *Opportunities for the use of locally grown timber in the South Yorkshire Forest.* South Yorkshire Forest Project, Sheffield.

Booker, J. and Tittensor, R. 1992 Coppicing for nature conservation – the practical reality. In G. P. Buckley (ed) *Ecology and Management of Coppice Woodlands,* Chapman and Hall, pp. 299-305, London.

Bownes, J. S., Riley, T. H., Rotherham, I. D. and Vincent, S. M. 1991 *Sheffield Nature Conservation Strategy.* Sheffield City Council, Sheffield.

Eccles, C. 1986 *South Yorkshire: Inventory of Ancient Woodland.* Nature Conservancy Council, Peterborough.

Evelyn, John 1706 *Sylva or a Discourse of Forest-Trees.* 4th edition. Scott, Chiswell, Sawbridge and Tooke, London.

Gilbert, O. L. 1982 The management of urban woodland in Sheffield. *The Sorby Record,* **20,** 47-48.

Hall, T. W. 1937 *Incunabula of Sheffield History.* J. W. Northend Ltd., Sheffield.

Hambler, C. and Speight, M. R. 1995 Biodiversity Conservation in Britain: Science replacing Tradition. *British Wildlife* **17,** 137-147.

Historical Manuscripts Commission 29 1901 *Portland Manuscripts VI.*

Jones, M. 1984 Woodland Origins in a South Yorkshire Parish. *The Local Historian,* **16,** 73-82.

Jones, M. 1986a Ancient Woods in the Sheffield area: the documentary evidence. *The Sorby Record* **24,** 7-18.

Jones, M. 1986b *Sheffield's Ancient Woods, Past and Present.* Sheffield City Polytechnic. Report for Sheffield City Council.

Jones, M. 1988 Broad Ing Plantation: survey and management plan. Sheffield City Polytechnic. Report for CARE Project/Tankersley Parish Council.

Jones, M. 1989-92 *Inventory Survey of Ancient Woods in Rotherham Metropolitan Borough, 3 Vols.* Sheffield City Polytechnic. Report for Rotherham MBC Planning Department.

Jones, M. 1993a South Yorkshire's Ancient Woodland: the Historical Evidence. In P. Beswick and I. D. Rotherham (eds) *Ancient Woodlands: their Archaeology and Ecology, a Coincidence of Interest, Landscape Archaeology and Ecology* **1,** 26-48.

Jones, M. 1993b *Sheffield's Woodland Heritage.* 2nd Edition. Green Tree Publications, Rotherham.

Jones, M. 1996 Deer in South Yorkshire: An Historical Perspective. *Journal of Practical Ecology and Conservation, Special Publication No. 1,* 11-26.

Jones, M. 1997 Woodland management on the Duke of Norfolk's Sheffield estate in the early eighteenth century. In M. Jones (ed) *Aspects of Sheffield: Discovering Local History, Vol. 1.* Wharncliffe Publishing Ltd., Barnsley.

Jones, M. 1998 The rise, decline and extinction of spring wood management in south-west Yorkshire. In C. Watkins (ed) *European Woods and Forests: Studies in Cultural History*. CAB International, Oxford.

Jones, M. and Jones, J. L. 1985 Traditional Woodland Management in the Sheffield area: an introductory survey. *Transactions of the Hunter Archaeological Society* **13**, 1-9.

Jones, M. and Talbot, E. 1995 Coppicing in urban woodlands: a progress report on a multi-purpose feasibility study in the City of Sheffield. *Journal of Practical Ecology and Conservation* **1**, 48-54.

Jones, M. and Walker, P. 1997 From coppice-with-standards to high forest: the management of Ecclesall Woods 1715-1901. In I. D. Rotherham and M. Jones (eds) *The Natural History of Ecclesall Woods, Pt. 1, Peak District Journal of Natural History and Archaeology, Special Publication No. 1*, 11-20.

Latham, I. D. 1994 *A desk top assessment of the archaeological potential of the Wharncliffe Forest*. South Yorkshire Archaeology Unit. Report for South Yorkshire Project.

Rackham, O. 1980 *Ancient Woodland: its history, vegetation and uses in England*. Edward Arnold, London.

Riley, D 1980 *Early Landscapes from the Air*. University of Sheffield, Sheffield.

Ronksley, J. G. (ed) *An exact and perfect Survey and View of the Manor of Sheffield with other lands by John Harrison, 1637*. Robert White and Co., Worksop.

Rotherham, I. D. 1996 Woods in the heart of a city. *Yorkshire Wildlife*, Autumn issue, 10-12.

South Yorkshire Forest Team 1994 *South Yorkshire Forest Plan*. South Yorkshire Forest Project, Sheffield.

South Yorkshire Forest Partnership 1997 *Fuelling a Revolution - the Woods that Founded the Steel Country (Restoring the South Yorkshire Forest's Heritage Woods)*. Application to the Heritage Lottery Fund No. 96 - 00700. South Yorkshire Forest Partnership, Sheffield.

Spray, M. 1981 Holly as a Fodder in England. *Agricultural History Review* **29**, 97-110.

Spray, M. and Smith, D. J. 1977 The rise and fall of holly in the Sheffield region. *Transactions of the Hunter Archaeological Society* **10**, 239-51.

Chapter 6

Medieval Woodland in North Yorkshire

Tom Gledhill

Introduction

The aim of this chapter is to make a critical study of the information available from documentary sources to provide an overview of woodland distribution and management in North Yorkshire. A number of sources provide evidence for medieval woodland. These include place-name evidence; the record provided by Domesday Book; and later medieval documentary evidence, in particular monastic charters and other documents recording rights to, and ownership of land. All these sources have their interpretational challenges. This is as much a study of the nature of the evidence, as of the woodland itself.

Sources; Their Nature and Interpretation

Domesday Book would seem at first glance to give the clearest possible picture of woodland just after the Norman Conquest (Fig. 6.1). For each Vill (approximately equivalent to a modern Civil Parish) the length and breadth of woodland is given; and it is categorised into different types. The first problem with this is in converting the length and breadth into acreages (a triangular woodland would have half the area of a rectangular woodland of the same length and breadth). This has been solved by Oliver Rackham (1980) by assuming an average shape for Domesday woodland. This appears to work quite well for many counties, but for North Yorkshire there are problems. As Rackham (1980) points out, the entry for the manor of Pickering is the largest woodland entry in Domesday; so large in fact that this, when converted to acres implies that the Tabular Hills and the Moors were largely wooded. This is contradicted by evidence from pollen preserved in peat bogs, which shows that the tops of the moors were mostly cleared of trees during the Bronze and Iron Ages (Atherden, 1976).

The other sources also have their inherent problems of interpretation. The medieval charters and inquisitions seldom give the size of the woods concerned, so that it is difficult to judge whether an area with sparse references reflects a small number of large woods, or whether an area with many references reflects many

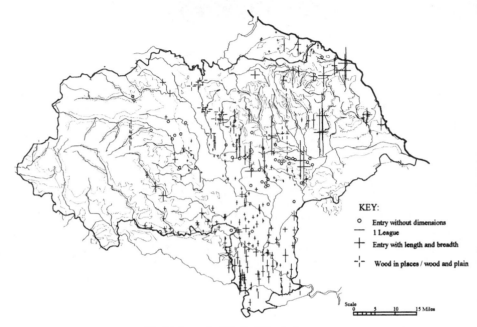

KEY:

○   Entry without dimensions

—   1 League

✛   Entry with length and breadth

⫯   Wood in places / wood and plain

Scale
0   5   10   15 Miles

Fig 6.1 Domesday Woodland Distribution.

small woods. The distribution of references may also reflect the distribution of monastic holdings, as much of the evidence derives from monastic chartularies. This may not be a major problem; monastic holdings covered a large part of the county, and an ecclesiastical bias is to some extent balanced by the use of fines, inquisitions, and such lay charter material as is available. Forest areas, particularly private forests and the less important royal forests, tend to have very vague references to woodland, rights to timber, wood, or pasture being exercised (on paper at least) over the whole forest rather than a particular woodland.

The majority of surviving place-names in England were coined during the period of Anglo-Saxon and Scandinavian settlement between about 500 and 1000 AD. Many of these place-names described the landscape which the new settlers inherited. Some of the Old English and Norse words used in place-names are related to woodland and can be mapped to give an impression of the distribution of woodland in the late first millennium AD (Fig. 6.2). A wide variety of these place-name elements exist; however the number of place-names in North Yorkshire with published derivations involving these is very small. The coverage of the Place-Name Society volumes for Yorkshire is neither complete nor systematic, but represents a collection of names apparently selected because of their philological

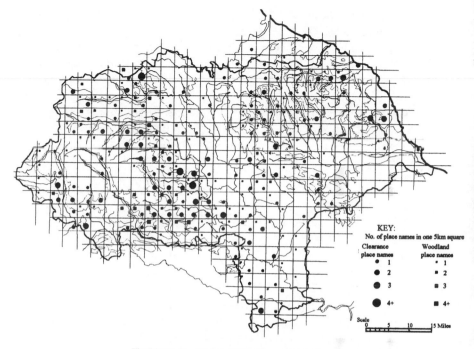

Fig 6.2 Woodland Related Place Names Distribution.

interest, or because they are perceived to be representative of a type. As a result place-names have been used in this study which do not have recognised derivations or ancient spellings. This creates both problems and opportunities. The greatest problem is plainly that of insecure derivations. Careful selection of place-name elements can minimise this difficulty. Some elements, such as *bearu* have been avoided altogether because of the potential for confusion; or in the case of *wudu* because a form of this is still in use. In other cases situations where confusion might arise can be avoided. An instance of this concerns place-names involving 'ley' (or ly). Although the majority of these are assumed to be derived from *leah* (a clearing or wood), a proportion are likely to derive from *law* (hill). As a result ley names which obviously refer to hills, such as the two Viewly Hills in the Vale of York, are omitted. A similar possibility for confusion arises from names involving 'with', which can be derived from *vithr* (wood) or *wath* (ford). Two examples of the name Sandwith are excluded for this reason; in one case Smith (1961, p. 236) gives a derivation from *wath*, and in the other such a derivation can be expected from the location. *Carr* has been avoided because in North Yorkshire this may refer to peat bog rather than the more usual alder woodland. The choice of place-name elements is further affected by the necessity to achieve a reasonable balance between Old English and Old Norse terms in order to avoid highlighting differences in the cultural identity of settlers or the period of settlement, rather than contrasts in the appearance of the landscape. In view of all these considerations the following list of place-name elements was chosen for mapping (Table 6.1)

Element	Meaning	Equivalents in modern spelling
leah	clearing or wood	ley, ly, laugh. (not used where *law* probable derivation)
thwait	clearing	thwait, waite.
weald	woodland	wold, wald. (see below)
scaga	wood	shaw, saw.
scogr	wood	scoe, skew, sque.
vithr	wood	with (except where derivation from *wath* probable)
lundr	wood	lund, lunt.
fridd	wood	frith

Table 6.1 Place-name elements mapped

Wold is used with extreme caution in the North Yorkshire Wolds, where the term is applied to chalk downland.

Although the relationship between clearance place-names and woodland is well established, it is possible to propose additional variables which may have influenced the pattern of clearing and wood elements in place-names. A consideration of these takes our understanding a step further than a simple correlation of clearance names with former woodland. It is particularly important to do this for North Yorkshire as this is a county with relatively few clearance names, yet there are obvious contrasts between different areas of the Domesday map of the county. Patterns of settlement might, for instance, be expected to produce very different patterns of clearance or wood names for the same overall woodland density. This type of contrast is illustrated by the simple diagrams in Fig. 6.3.

The woodland is represented by the shaded areas. It can be seen that dispersed clearings will have a greater tendency to generate clearance names, and might also generate a greater density of wood names. Such differences in the arrangement of clearances might be caused by environmental factors such as the relative disposition of good and marginal land, or by the pattern of clearance inherited from the late Roman period. It is also possible that names were lost in the transition from dispersed to nucleated settlement.

Topography would also be expected to exert some influence; the more prominent the woodland in the landscape, the more likely settlement is to be named

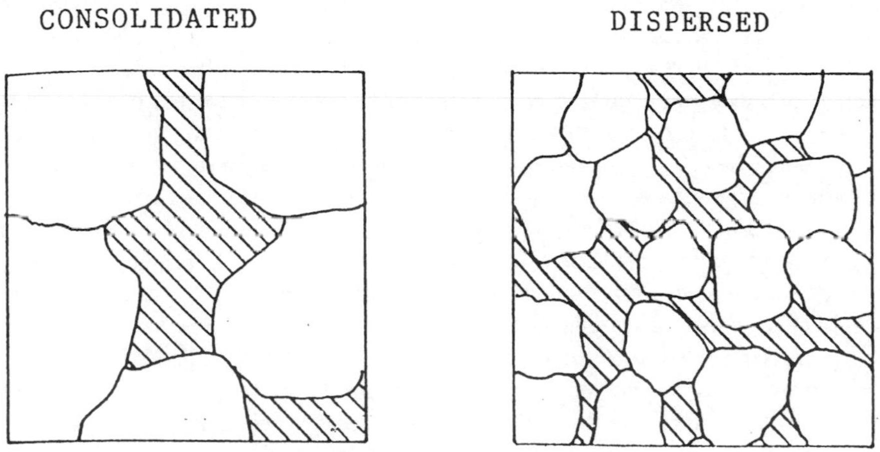

CONSOLIDATED

DISPERSED

Fig 6.3 Place Names and Settlement.

GORGE

DALE

LOWLAND

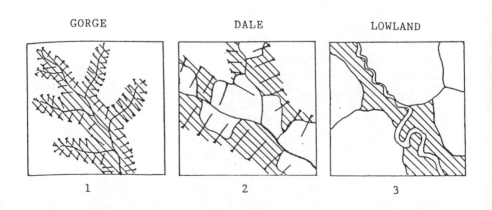

1

2

3

Fig 6.4 Place Names and Topography

after it, and the more likely its own name is to survive. Woods hidden away in steep-sided gorges are less likely to be remembered. It is thus possible to model the probable effect of clearance patterns and topography on different landscape types (Fig. 6.4). The situation in diagram 1 will give rise to relatively few clearance place-names, and even the woods may be expected to receive the name of the gorges which contain them, as it is this that is the distinctive feature. Diagram 2 represents a situation where both clearance and wood names are likely to be more frequent than the average for a given proportion of woodland. Most of the settlements appear to be in clearings, and woods are prominent features in the landscape. The more consolidated lowland settlement reflected in diagram 3 would produce relatively few clearance names. The woods are prominent features of the landscape, but would only generate a few names applicable to large areas.

In making a comparison between the evidence for woodland in medieval documents, place-names, and Domesday, it is necessary to assume that all these represent stages in a more or less continuous process of woodland clearance. Such an assumption is reasonable because of the abundant evidence for agricultural and population expansion during this period, which would have allowed little opportunity for the formation of secondary woodland. If this premise is accepted then it is reasonable to assume that a woodland recorded in say 1300 was present in

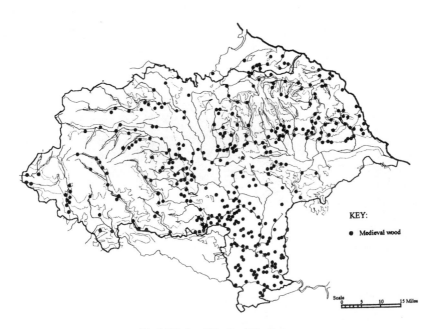

Fig 6.5 Medieval Woodland Distribution.

1086, whether the woodland is recorded in Domesday Book or not. Similarly the situation in 1086 was the product of what went before, and although clearance may have occurred in the meantime, major concentrations of woodland reflected in place-names would be expected to survive till Domesday. One consequence of accepting these overall assumptions is that it renders less important the fact that neither the medieval documents nor the place-name evidence represent a defined point in time (Figure 6.5).

Domesday, an Interpretation

Comparison of the maps of place-name and medieval charter information with the map of Domesday entries shows that in some areas the correspondence between the three is good. There is little evidence for woodland in the areas of the Yorkshire Wolds, the Cleveland Plain, and the Vale of Mowbray on any of the maps. In other areas however, the maps differ. In many cases the differences are explicable by the insufficiencies of the evidence of the place-names or the medieval documentation. An instance of this is the Vale of York, where a very wooded landscape is recorded by Domesday, and supported by the medieval documents, but is not reflected in the place-name evidence. This underestimate of the amount of woodland in the place-name evidence might be expected for this lowland area with nucleated settlement on the basis of the model put forward earlier. Many of the dales along the southern edge of the North York Moors may have resembled the situation in diagram 1 (Figure 6.4), with the result that place-names underestimate the degree to which the landscape was wooded. There are, however, other areas where the accuracy of Domesday is open to question. In the Pennine Dales, for instance, place-name evidence and the medieval documentation would imply a reasonable amount of woodland, whereas Domesday records very little. Domesday fails to record any woodland whatsoever for Craven, whereas the other forms of evidence imply a moderate amount, though less than in the Dales.

The comparison between the maps makes it possible to determine the areas in which the Domesday record is reasonably good, and those where it is less so. This raises the question of why Domesday might misrepresent the distribution of woodland. In the case of Craven an obvious reason arises out of the Domesday text. Details are given only for the value and ownership in 1066; entries for 1086 are entirely lacking. Since the woodland is usually only recorded in the 1086 entries, it is hardly surprising that there is no record of woodland for Craven. In other areas some error also arises from the way in which the Domesday entry has been transferred to the map. An instance of this is where woodland from a large number of vills is combined in a single entry. This is the case for the anomalous entry for Pickering. This may not refer purely to Pickering itself (in which case the whole vill was woodland), but more likely to Pickering, its four bailiwicks and the further 18 vills which belonged to it *in soc*. Redistributing the woodland in this way would certainly make more sense in the context of the medieval record. Pickering is in fact only one of a number of vills with extensive socages or bailiwicks which have very large entries of woodland areas recorded for them and their bailiwicks. Other important examples are Allerton, Sherburn,Whitby and Falsgrave. In all of these cases, the Domesday record would be more consistent with the medieval documentation if the woodland were redistributed to the vills *in soc*.

The explanation for the apparent under-recording of woodland in the Yorkshire Dales may lie in the distribution of what Domesday refers to as 'waste'. If the distribution of this is compared to that of Domesday woodland it is apparent that woodland is rare in most of the areas where waste is common. In general waste seems to indicate a lack of value, and is often associated with a lack of recorded population (a lack of direct value to the lord is indicated by the later medieval use of 'waste' to indicate common land; this is now reflected in place-names such as Thorne Waste, South Yorks.). Domesday waste may have covered a number of differing situations. In the Pennine Dales, vills may have been described as waste because in these areas Norman control was not yet very strong, settlement was not very advanced, and Scottish raids may have caused some destruction, with the result that rents were difficult to collect and these vills were of little or no value (Wightman, 1970). As one of the main functions of Domesday appears to have been to assess landed revenue, it should be no surprise that woodland which was difficult to exploit was often not recorded.

Wooded and Unwooded Landscapes in Medieval North Yorkshire
We are now in a position to distinguish several distinct landscapes in North Yorkshire, differentiated by different concentrations and dispositions of woodland (Figure 6.6). The Vale of Mowbray, the Vale of Pickering, and the Wolds appear to have had very little woodland by Domesday. This situation already appears to have been reached before the period when the area received its Germanic and Scandinavian place-names. These areas may thus have had open landscapes in the late Roman and early post-Roman periods. In contrast to these 'woodless' areas is the Vale of York (including the lower Wharfe Valley) in which extensive areas of woodland were attached to most vills. In the eastern fringe of the Pennines most vills had some woodland; but many of these woods may have been relatively small. In the Dales the woodland was probably mainly confined to the steep valley sides, but may have been widespread in these locations. Craven probably had rather less woodland than the Dales, but it may have been in similar locations. A similar pattern might be proposed for Eskdale, and the upper portions of other moorland dales where they broaden out north of the Tabular Hills. The western scarp of the North York Moors was well wooded, as was the northern side of the Howardian Hills. Along the northern edge of the Vale of Pickering the lack of woodland and clearance elements in place-names, and the narrowness of certain Domesday

Fig 6.6 Woodland Landscapes in North Yorkshire.

entries, leads us to conclude that woodland may have been mainly confined to steep sided gorges and the southern scarp of the Tabular Hills.

Woodland Management at Domesday

Yorkshire is one of only a few counties for which Domesday Book distinguishes between different types of woodland. The main categories are *silva pastilis* and *silva minuta* (Figure 6.7). The first of these, *silva pastilis,* is of fairly obvious economic importance, and is translated as woodpasture (Rackham, 1980). *Silva minuta* is translated as 'underwood' by Darby and Maxwell (1962) and Farrer (1912). This may imply a connection with coppicing, as suggested by Rackham (1980), or some kind of scrub. Entries described as *silva* are also fairly frequent. Domesday Book occasionally further qualifies the entry, as in *silva pastilis per loca* (e.g. the sokelands of Easingwold). To assume, as Rackham does, that this refers to a wood which is partly woodpasture and partly coppice would seem to be stretching the evidence too far. The rendering by Farrer (1912) of 'pasturable wood in places' is more satisfactory. Similarly the translation of *silva modica* as coppice by Darby and Maxwell (1962) must be incorrect, as this would make nonsense of the entry for Crayke: '*silva pastilis modica*'. Farrer must therefore be correct in giving 'small pasturable wood' as the translation.

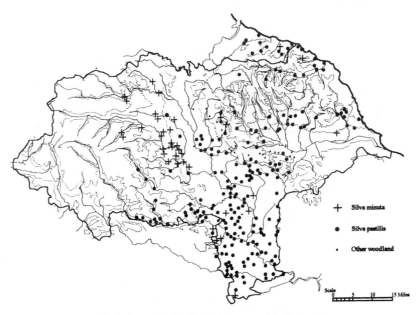

Fig 6.7 Domesday Woodland Management, Distribution Map.

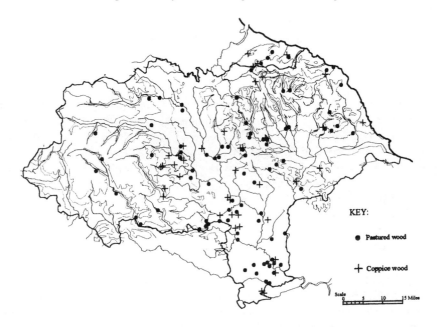

Fig 6.8 Medieval Woodland Management, Distribution Map.

It is clear from the map that pastured woodland was by far the most important in terms both of area and distribution (Figure 6.8). The evidence for coppice woodland is less clear. It is tempting to concur with Rackham in his assessment of the significance of *silva minuta* woods, particularly in view of their predominance in the Ripon area which had dense settlement and many small woods.

Medieval Woodland Management: Interpreting the Sources
Before attempting to discuss medieval woodland management it is necessary to formulate a procedure for the interpretation of the medieval documentation. To do this we first have to assume that medieval practice divides neatly into woodpasture and coppice. Whilst this does not represent the true medieval situation, the resultant map may be of some benefit in illustrating regional variation in management practice. The application of defined criteria for interpretation makes it possible to make an appraisal of the evidence and the accuracy with which it is likely to portray the management of medieval North Yorkshire's woods.

Medieval documents which mention woodland vary considerably in the degree to which management information is given. Where coppicing is concerned three main classes of evidence are available. Unambiguous references to coppice are those in which the process of cutting and subsequently enclosing the wood are explicitly mentioned. One such reference is a sale of wood at Aislaby which requires the purchasers to leave five wavers (young timber trees) and as many holly trees, and to enclose the wood at their own cost for five years (Clay, 1940, p. 1). Just six references of this type were found in the documentary material studied. The rarity of such references should not be a surprise. It must have been very unusual for this type of transaction to find its way into permanent records of property such as chartularies or fines.

References to woodland enclosure may also be regarded as evidence for coppicing, as coppices had to be enclosed after cutting to prevent animals damaging the new growth. A total of 43 references were found which referred to woodland enclosure. The quality of these varied considerably. At best, as in the six references mentioned above, enclosure is expressly to protect coppice. A second set of 17 references imply the distinctive enclosure of the whole wood, often with the intention of excluding animals. One problem with this type of reference is that a proportion may refer to parks rather than coppice woods. This is the case at Priors Cliff, Guisborough, (Brown, 1889, p. 116) as there are later references to a park. In some cases where enclosure is mentioned it is not clear whether the intention is to enclose the land from the wood or *vice versa,* in others the primary function of boundary features appears to be the demarcation of property. For the purposes of interpreting coppice only those references which explicitly refer to coppice, and those which imply the distinctive enclosure of the whole wood and/or the exclusion of pasturing animals (except when they can be shown to be parks) are admissible.

Wood names can also be used to infer coppice management. *Hagg* (or *hag*) and *fall* are both terms used to describe a coppice compartment which were used in medieval wood names in North Yorkshire. *Hagg* needs to be used with some caution as an indicator of management, as it appears in a number of other contexts. The most important of these are peat cuttings, often referred to as peat hags, and intakes. A large number of this latter use can be found in surveys and maps of Bilsdale (Ashcroft & Hill, 1980; Ashcroft, 1983). These are, however, unlikely to form a high proportion of wood names. In South Yorkshire *hag* is used to refer to holly woods which supplied winter fodder for stock (see Jones, Chapter 5). This use does not appear to have been common in North Yorkshire. The occurrence of *hagg* and *fall* names in the medieval documentary record for North Yorkshire is not common. A total of only 17 references dated before 1400 was found.

The burden of evidence for woodpasture is a good deal lighter than for coppice, mostly consisting of references to pasturing animals. Given that coppice often involves pasture at some time in the cycle there is bound to be some confusion here. In general, where a wood has evidence of both it has been treated as coppice.

Trends in Woodland Economy
Woodland utilisation not only varies spatially but also through time. Figure 6.9 represents the frequency with which pannage (the practice of taking pigs into the woods in autumn to feed on acorns and beech mast), pasture, and coppice are referred to at different dates. The information is expressed for overlapping periods of 60 years. This ensures that each point represents a proportion of at least 31 references, and has the advantage of ironing out wild fluctuations to reveal the underlying trends.

The graph can be divided into three time periods labelled A, B, and C. During period A references to pannage are most frequent, during B pasture, and during C coppice. This is unlikely to be a direct measure of the degree to which pannage etc. were practised, but rather the importance placed on them by the landlord, whose priorities the documentary record generally reflects. The relative importance of pannage during period A can be interpreted as indicating a low level of management, that mast bearing trees were frequent, and coppiced and pollarded woods rare. During period B the importance of pannage declined relative to the total number of woodland references. This must represent a change of priorities, if not management. Pasture is the most frequently recorded woodland use in this period, probably reflecting an increasing need to manage and control woodland pasture. In this context the best interpretation of the decline of pannage is that tree management, particularly pollarding and the compartmentation of woodpasture, was increasing, with the result that there were fewer mature, mast-bearing trees. Interpretation of the final phase, C, is complicated by the scarcity of references. There appears to be an increasing interest in coppice, and a marked decline in the

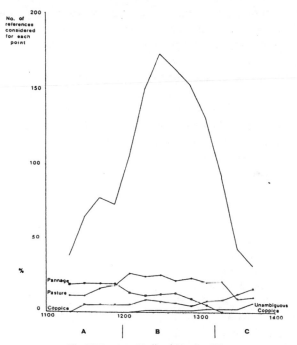

Fig 6.9 Trends in Medieval Woodland Economy.

frequency with which woodpasture is mentioned. This decline is contemporary with the early 14th century agricultural decline, culminating in the Black Death. These events almost certainly led to a slump in the demand for pasture of all kinds including woodpasture.

The documentary record thus appears to show a gradual shift from pannage and woodpasture to coppice. Similarly if we look at the medieval management map, pannage references are concentrated in the areas which had most woodland at Domesday. The evidence for coppice, on the other hand, is concentrated in an area of the Pennine fringe, where there was a relatively smaller density of woodland, and which has little evidence for pannage.

Woodland at the Dissolution
For the 16th century a wealth of documentary material is available, of which the most important is a series of Crown surveys of woods belonging to dissolved monasteries. These surveys illustrate the same set of woodland management techniques as were in use in the medieval period. Thus at Selby in 1540 the common woodpasture or outwood still existed, containing 1300 'scrude' (pollard?) oaks and four coppices, of which two lay in the common pasture, while the others were 'springed' (coppiced). There were also several other coppices not in the common pasture.

115

The detailed information in the surveys allows a much more confident interpretation of management than was possible for the medieval material. It is not however possible to construct a meaningful map of this material, as there is a much less even coverage than that of the medieval charters and Domesday. The solution is to select a number of smaller areas for comparison. In the Vale of York, Selby and Hambleton are suitable subjects for study. Four woods were recorded at Hambleton at the dissolution. These included the Outwood or woodpasture in which the king's tenants had common pasture and hedgebote, and Hambleton Haugh, an oak coppice apparently without timber. Of the two remaining woods Est Hagge [*sic*] is described as having very fair holly underwood and many old 'runted' oaks, and was used by the king's tenants there as common. The combination of common rights, a coppice name, holly underwood with old or pollarded oak, suggests that this was a coppice compartment within a woodpasture (probably the Outwood). King Spring on the other hand is a small coppice with both timber trees and mixed underwood. At Selby the Outwood with its oak pollards and four haggs has already been mentioned; in addition a medieval park called Stainer Park had three coppice woods, and there was one more small coppice called the Carr. The Outwoods of Selby and Hambleton have medieval origins, East Hagg and King Spring are not recorded before the sixteenth century, Hambleton Haugh appears to have been a woodpasture in medieval times, and Stainer Park is what remains of a larger medieval wood which was divided up between freeholders in lieu of common when the park was created towards the end of the

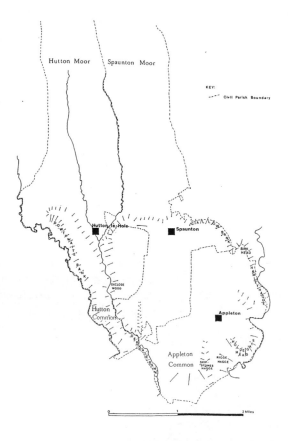

Fig 6.10 Woods in Spaunton in 1545.

116

thirteenth century. In conclusion, therefore, although many of the medieval woods in this area survived to the sixteenth century there was a definite shift away from woodpasture to coppice.

At Marrick in Swaledale the foundation charter of Marrick priory (Clay, 1936) mentions woods and assarts within woods, giving the impression of a wooded environment. By the sixteenth century the woods were islands in cleared land, very much as they are today. Of the eleven woods which remained in the sixteenth century ten were coppices. The remaining wood, Oxe Close, was of rather uncertain status. It is probable that most of the woodland clearance took place soon after the foundation of the priory. However, where management is concerned many of the wood names of the sixteenth century such as Colte Park, Oxe Close, Shepe Bank, suggest an earlier phase of woodpasture exploitation.

North-east Yorkshire is represented by the area surrounding the village of Spaunton. Here medieval references suggest that the dominant form of management at this time was woodpasture (Table 6.2). A large number of woods were recorded in the sixteenth century; many of these can be identified and mapped (see Figure 6.10).

Coppice	Woodpasture	Other
Birk Head	Spyres Wood	Stokynt Closes
Hamley Hagge	Gallow Bank	Dowthwaite Bank
Holdegate Head	Ampsters Wood (common)	Hutton Lytell Wood
Rygge Hagge	Hutton Oxeclose	
Skypstones Hagge	Depdale & Littledale End	
Hutton Hagge	Hutton Yaus	

Table 6.2   Woods in Spaunton in 1545

Stokynt closes are best interpreted as woodpasture which has been enclosed as they contain two hundred 'pollyd okes'. In contrast to Marrick the majority of the coppices have names in hagg, suggesting that coppicing was not such a recent development here. Place-names such as Waite, Ridding and Lund where no sixteenth century woodland is recorded, and a large woodland entry in Domesday Book point to a loss of woodland during the medieval period. Where management is concerned it is most likely that most of the coppice woods developed in the later Middle Ages, as the emphasis in medieval documents is on common right to wood, pasture, and pannage.

The best opportunity for study in the Pennine fringe is presented by the properties of the late Fountains Abbey. These were subject to a series of surveys during the sixteenth century (Walbran, 1863). Of 23 woods mentioned in these 17 were coppices, five of the remainder being woodpasture closes, and one a wooded meadow. Coppicing was therefore by far the most important method of woodland management at the time. Coppicing in this area may also have been of greater antiquity than elsewhere as it is this area which was notable for its woods with coppice names in medieval documents, and for its *silva minuta* woods at Domesday. The long history of coppice in this area is also reflected in the variety of coppice names (*hagg, fall,* and *spring* are all represented), and in the tautological combination Abbot Fall Spring.

In most areas, except perhaps the upper reaches of the Yorkshire Dales, there appears to have been a definite shift towards coppicing between the fourteenth and sixteenth centuries. In some areas, as at Marrick, this may have been a relatively late development. In others, as at Spaunton, and especially the Pennine fringe, coppicing appears to have been long established. Woodpasture on the other hand was in decline. Both at Marrick and on the Fountains Abbey estates, common woodpasture had almost disappeared, leaving a handful of woodpasture closes. At Spaunton, Ampsters Wood was still a common woodpasture, but Stokynt Closes, containing two hundred pollard oaks, points to the recent enclosure of woodpasture here too. It is the Vale of York where the tradition of common woodpastures appears to have been strongest, represented by the pollarded and compartmented Outwoods of Hambleton and Selby.

The apparent increase in the importance of coppice woods evident in these detailed studies is mirrored by a more general consideration of the sixteenth century evidence. The most convenient way of illustrating this is by the occurrence of coppice wood names. In the sixteenth century evidence 70 coppice names occur in approximately 350 references (i.e. 20%), compared to just 17 in the pre-1400 literature out of a total of *circa* 900 references (0.02%). A similar impression can be gained from the use of the word 'spring' as a wood name. This was a common term used to describe coppices in late medieval and modern times but was very uncommon in North Yorkshire before 1400. It is reasonable, therefore, to assume that coppices with spring names were created after 1400. On this basis the sixteenth-century evidence implies that the number of coppices at least doubled between 1400 and 1550. This amounts to a revolution in woodland management. The effects and intensity of this revolution varied from place to place, its causes were complex, but may have been linked to industrial expansion, and changes in the rural economy and the exercise of common rights after the Black Death (Gledhill, 1994).

Bibliography
Ashcroft, K. 1983: *Bilsdale Maps 1781 - 1857.* North Yorkshire County Records Office Publications 32.
Ashcroft, M. Y. & Hill, A. M. 1980: *Bilsdale Surveys 1637-1851.* North Yorkshire County Records Office Publications 23.
Atherden, M. A. 1976: The impact of late prehistoric cultures on the vegetation of

the North York Moors. *Transactions of the Institute of British Geographers*, **1**, 284-300.

Brown, W. ed. 1889: *The Guisborough Chartulary, Vol. 1*. Publications for the Surtees Society 86.

Clay, C.T. ed. 1936: *Early Yorkshire Charters, Volume 5, the Honour of Richmond Part 2*. Yorkshire Archaeological Society Extra Series **2**.

Clay, C.T. ed. 1940: *Yorkshire Deeds, Vol. 8*. Yorkshire Archaeological Society Records Series **102**.

Darby, H. C. & Maxwell, T. S. 1962: *The Domesday Geography of Northern England*. Cambridge.

Farrer, W. 1912: Domesday Survey. In *The Victoria History of the Counties of England, A History of the County of York. 2*, 133-327. Constable and Co.

Gledhill, T. D. 1994: *A Woodland History of North Yorkshire*. PhD. thesis Sheffield University.

Rackham, O. 1980: *Ancient Woodland*. Edward Arnold.

Smith, A. H. 1961: *Place Names of the West Riding of Yorkshire*, Parts 1-8. English Place Name Society.

Walbran, J. R. ed. 1863: *Memorials of the Abbey of St Mary of Fountains*. Publications of the Surtees Society **42**.

Wightman, W. E. 1970: The significance of waste in Yorkshire Domesday. *Northern History*, **5**, 55-71.

Chapter 7

Historic Woodland in the Vale of York

Jennifer Kaner

Introduction

The Yorkshire Philosophical Society Woodland History Group has chosen a few woods each year to explore and record. Originally inspired by a lecture given by Dr Rackham in 1981, it has turned a bunch of amateurs into a group reasonably well informed about woodland flora and as individuals into defenders of woods. Many of these woods have been in the Vale, which is not an ideal area. As soon as the hills start to rise towards the Howardian Hills or the Magnesian Limestone the woodland and the landscape become more interesting. Despite this, there are remnants of ancient woodland in the Vale and there are numerous documentary sources referring to woodland long vanished. It is these original sources, both in print and in manuscript that have been the focus of this study, in the hope that others can build on this research.

The Vale soils were laid down by the retreat of the glaciers and provide a wide variety of sands, clays and gravel. Each township is different, and along with the soil type quite small differences in height above sea level make large differences in waterlogging and the possible land uses. This must be borne in mind. In the Vale there are no steep wooded hillsides impossible to plough but there are areas which were peat moors or bogs and bands of acid soil.

Early documentary sources

There are few Anglo-Saxon charters for Yorkshire and only one, for Howden, has a topographical boundary clause describing a wood in the Vale of York. Though long gone, a rich hedge which may be a remnant of the woodland survives (Le Patourel, Long and Pickles, 1993, p.129). Part is certainly a park pale with some woodland flora and fungi.

King Edgar's grant of 'inland' to the Archbishop round Sherburn in Elmet in 923 and a list of the lands in the soc (Jurisdiction) of Sherburn from 1030 does shed some light on later Domesday book entries for Sherburn, where along with 96 carucates of land there was woodland pasture 8 leagues long and 3 leagues wide and coppice wood 4 leagues long and 1 wide, much the largest in the Vale of York

(Farrer, 1914; Faull and Stimson, 1986). Bishopwood still covered *c.* 846 acres in 1998.

Domesday Book
The Domesday Book records woodland, though in imprecise terms. However, by mapping the entries an impression can be given of areas wooded in 1086 (see Figure 6.1, previous chapter). There are dangers in that not all vills are named and others, described as waste, could have included woodland but at least it prompts questions. This exercise has been done (Darby and Maxwell, 1962; Gledhill, this volume). Using this information for the Vale of York there are three features that are worth noting. The first is the relative absence of woodland east of the Derwent in the East Riding (now East Yorkshire), though Howden does have a respectable 3 × 1 leagues of wood pasture. Secondly, there is a ring round York where little or no wood is recorded. Later records show that York cattle had the right to graze over the common lands of the townships adjoining York on the East of the Ouse. The same townships were described as paying tax with the city in 1086, so possibly the impact of York's cattle may have destroyed any possible regrowth of trees at a much earlier date. Boundary crosses mark the limit of this area (Tillott, 1961). Thirdly, the absence of wood in the sector to the north-east of the city takes more explaining, though here the information is ambiguous particularly for lands belonging to the Minster or Archbishop. The land is certainly low and was badly drained. Strensall Common remains as an example of the type of landscape that might have been usual, ie. lowland heath not woodland. It was this area that was later recorded as within the Forest of Galtres (Figure 7.1). Not all forests were wooded and it is possible that an area of relatively unproductive land near York and the royal estate of Easingwold would be a prime target for afforestation by the Normans and provide ample space for hunting. It may have survived longer than the other Vale forests because of its relative infertility.

The Forests of the Vale of York
Forests originally surrounded York on all sides: Galtres, Ouse and Derwent and Ainsty. The Forests of Ainsty and the Ouse and Derwent were both co-terminous with their wapentakes and had much more Domesday woodland than Galtres. Galtres may originally have covered most of the Wapentake of Bulmer though by 1316 it had shrunk to the land between the Foss, Ouse and Kyle. This meant land under Forest Law not necessarily full of trees. These forests first appear in the Pipe Rolls in the twelfth century and were described as ancient in 1230 (Close Rolls, 1902). Within these forests each township had its open fields and commons surrounded by land which was intercommoned by all the vills within the forest. The Crown could, within the forest boundaries, control the use of the land and its priority was the preservation of game. This involved keeping fences low and

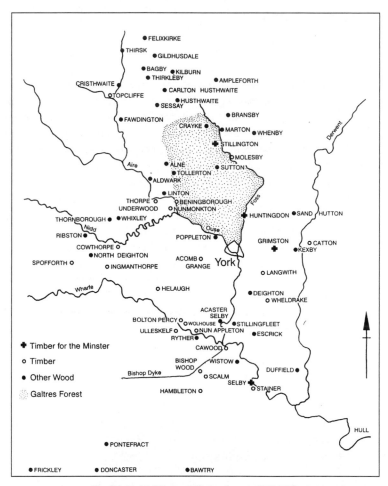

Fig. 7.1 York's Wood and Timber Sources 1250-1540

preventing people destroying trees and underwood, 'the vert', and enclosing tracts of land for their own use and thus reducing the area available for deer, 'assarting'. Licences could be bought from the king for assarting and fines were paid to the king for taking greenwood. Fines were also paid if a dog entered the forest without having his claws clipped. The Pipe Rolls are full of these fines. For example, the men of Beningborough,Whixley, Wigginton, and Towthorp were fined in 1166-7 or 1169-70 for taking green wood or vert and in 1175-6 the vills of Wheldrake, Elvington, Heslington, Newton on Ouse, Linton and Aldwark as well as many individuals paid fines for offences in the forest (Pipe Roll Society, 1889; 1892; 1904).

Ainsty was disafforested in 1190 when the inhabitants paid £30 16s. 11d. to King Richard I to be quit of the forest (Stenton, 1925). Pressure for the disafforestation of Ouse and Derwent came from the monastic landlords, particularly Fountains, which was building up an estate at Wheldrake. The charter of disafforestation, in 1234, was recorded in the Register of the Bishop of Durham and there is a vivid description of the results of the process in Norman French (Hardy, 1875): "And since when all the country was disafforested through the great ransom that the country gave to King Henry, son of King John ...each man between Use and Derwent might approve and inclose those wastes and make parks without disturbance, thereupon from that time there have been approvements made by all the lords of the vills small and great between the waters ..... without asking leave of the lords or of the tenants of the vills near or distant; but that the free tenants who hold according to the ancient bounds of the vill where the approvement is made may have a share according to the quantity of their tenements because they contributed to the ransom.....and ....each vill between Sogfleet and the bridge of Battle may common in all seasons in moors and in woods and in wastes that lie uninclosed except in the Haye of Langwathe". A stream of assarts followed providing a ring of *ridding* names, often with the names of the men who made them, around the original core of open fields. Wheldrake, Escrick, Thorganby, Deighton and Riccall all have examples. The arguments between the townships and between different monastic landlords about rights to common also appear in the documents, as do the agreements where the freeholders handed their rights over to the landlord, who was usually monastic.

Langwith Hay remained as a refuge for the king's deer. Eighty years earlier his officers had provided venison, 50 roes and 50 hinds and charcoal from there, when King Henry III spent Christmas at York in 1251 (*Calendar of Liberate Rolls, 1959,* p. 8; *Close Rolls,* 1928, p.3, 27). Timber was given to the Archbishop in 1237 and used for the King's Works in York at various dates including 40 oaks in 1249 (*Close Rolls,* 1922, p.165). By 1269/70 Henry III was considering giving the Hay away and had an inquisition made by 12 knights and freemen from townships round the Hay as to whether it would damage the king if he granted it to his son. They said he would lose the herbage and pannage perhaps 40s. perhaps nothing according to the mast of acorns .... They estimated that within the covert there were 4000 oaks. They had estimated the number of acres because they were unable to measure the hay on account of an inundation (Brown, 1892, p.111-2).

Henry III actually gave it, in the foundation charter, to the Abbey of Vale Royale[1] or Darnhall, a Cistercian foundation in Cheshire. They passed it on to Warter Priory in the East Riding who sold it to the Dean and Chapter of York (English, 1996, p.80; Warter Cartulary; Dugdale, 1846, p.709). At first, the Dean

---

[1] Vale Royale was an offshoot of Abbey Dore.

and Chapter leased it to the Archbishops but by 1371 when the Dean and Chapter's surviving chamberlains' rolls start, 3,500 faggots from Langwith were being given to the 8 resident Minster canons. The rolls show that, during the 14th century, an extensive woodland was being managed. Eight thousand faggots were cut every year for the canons and later an additional 1000 for the choristers and 1000 to Wheldrake for tithe. There was a ditch round the Hay which was cleaned out, and a hedge and gates which were repaired. Timber went to build York Minster, 24 oaks in 1289, 20 oaks in 1396, 4 oak saplings in 1442-3. These records, perhaps the best surviving run for a Vale of York woodland, show that faggots not charcoal were the most important product. The wood was managed for producing this underwood as the care taken to repair the hedges and the gates shows. There are payments for cutting and carrying the 'rise', repairing the hedges, stripping bark for sale and byrtyning (chopping up) the branches for sale as faggots. 500 bundles were made from 24 oaks. A custodian was paid to look after the wood but as time passed the pasturage was being let out and was later leased for a period of years.

There is very little evidence of selling of wood by the Dean and Chapter but the faggots may have been sold on by the canons. In 1471, 4 canons received 15,000 faggots and astil wood [2]. The same system continued till the chamberlain rolls stop in the seventeenth century. There are records of a regular production of faggots or "kyddes", regular hedging and ditching as well as mending the way for the kydd waynes. By the late sixteenth century there is little evidence of timber being available as, when the Dean and Chapter needed a frame for a new house at Bishop Burton, they bought 6 trees from Thorpe Underwood, brought them from there to York and sent them to Bishop Burton by water and cart as a prefabricated frame! (York Minster Library, Chamberlains Accounts). During the Civil War much destruction was done. There had been "a great number of timber trees ......in the time of rebellion all these woods and underwoods were cut down and destroyed". The registrar of the Dean and Chapter should have had "20 loads of wood yerely as a fee due to his place" but could not have it because of the destruction. He had therefore left the reservation of the wood and underwood out of the lease. It was being argued that the lease was therefore void (Bodleian Library, Tanner MS 150). During the eighteenth century, the wood was leased out and a gamekeeper appointed but most of the area had become arable and pasture. From 1811 it was leased by the Yarboroughs of Heslington with the timber reserved to the Dean and Chapter. The Yarboroughs finally bought it from the Ecclesiastical Commissioners in 1859 by which time only 33 acres called Black wood survived. The block of woodland is now even smaller. It looks like a conifer plantation but there are still a

---

[2] A faggot was a statutory measure in the assize of fuel. Every faggot, bend or stick ought to contain in length 3 ft and the bond of every such faggott ought to be 24" about beside the knot. The bundles were tied with withies sometimes made of hazel. A kydd is an equivalent local term. Astilwood may have been smaller twigs or slivers of wood.

few bluebells *(Hyacinthoides non-scripta)*, primroses *(Primula vulgaris)*, wood sorrel *(Oxalis acetosella)*, wood anemone *(Anemone nemorosa)* and violet *(Viola riviniana)* and a large ditch on the boundary.

Langwith Hay was originally enclosed because it belonged to the king. Other assarts needed licences which usually required that the hedge should be kept low. There are examples from the Forest of Galtres from 1230 and 1234. For example, 200 acres formerly held by Henry de Helm, could be asserted and broken up and tilled for the extension of the king's demesne there. Earlier in 1231, he and his men of Huby had been granted estovers (necessaries) such as husbote, haybote and pasture for animals within Galtres and 10 acres of wood in which the oaks and timber had been cut and felled to make a hedge which the deer can leave and enter. This then was the pattern, a gradual process of turning uncultivated unenclosed land into private property for cultivation or for enclosed woodland. The process continued until Galtres was finally disafforested in 1629/30. Within this area what happened to the woodland cover?

In the reigns of Henry III and Edward I there were numerous grants of timber from Galtres by the Crown to, among others, the Templars and St Mary's to repair mills in York, to the Prior of Marton, the nuns of Wilberfoss, to the houses of Friars for repairs and for building as well as orders for charcoal when the king spent Christmas in York, as at Langwith. However, a major gift of 500 oaks to repair the staithes at Ravensrod in 1343 may have been among the last as when the Sheriff of the county, Ralph de Hastings in 1339, needed timber to make "engines" he bought the wood from the woods of the Archbishop, St Leonards, St Mary's and Selby Abbey. None came from Galtres (Public Record Office: E101.597.24).

It seems possible then that by this date timber trees, defined as more than 2ft in girth (Rackham, 1991, p.10), were in short supply though in 1369-70 21 oaks from the Forest were used to make "a bay and a flodegate" for the Castle Mills along with timber from Thorpe Underwood (Public Record Office E101.501.13).

The forest may have hit the problem that is created when animals have free access to both the seedlings and the regrowth of coppice, 'the spring'. Deer were free to come and go everywhere and cattle could be pastured on all the common land so, within the forest, woodland was only likely to survive where the crown had given licences to hedge it and ditch it and create a park or a private woodland. In the Forest of Galtres the examples are few but clear. Crayke and Marton which were emparked rather than being managed woodland, Overton and Beningborough.

At Overton, (Domesday: woodland pasture 1 league × 2 furlongs) the Abbot paid 40 marks and a palfrey to King John in 1204 for a licence to enclose his wood of Overton and make a park by the ancient bounds between the wood and the vills of Beningborough, Shipton and Skelton (Stenton, 1940: p.189; Drake, 1736: p.623). It seems likely that the wood, still a significant block in the Vale of York (118 acres), was originally much more extensive, as, in *c.* 1142-54, there was a dispute between Overton and Shipton and Beningborough over the boundary between wood and plain (*bosco et plano*). Then between 1161 and 1184 the Abbot of St Mary's had granted St Peter's, later St Leonard's Hospital 2 acres of land next to the 'rivum' (stream) between "our wood of Overton and the vill of Beningborough", presumably part of the same dispute. The Woodland History Group found a wood bank on the northern edge of the wood which we assumed must be the outer boundary and so had to try and explain why the apparent bounds of the wood were different from the original charter (Greenway, 1972, p.207; Farrer, 1914, p.148; Yorkshire Philosophical Society, 1993, p.69-72). Since then, we have discovered that banks of a similar nature extend through the wood so although, because of access problems since the wood was sold by the Forestry Commission, we have been unable to measure these or map them, I would like to suggest that the banks mark coppice departments and that further compartments earlier extended to the Beningborough boundary. The coppices were recorded by name at the Dissolution of the Monasteries. There were 9 totalling 163 acres with another 20 acres elsewhere (Public Record Office: SC 12.22.93). The park is not recorded among Overton field names but survives as a field name in both Skelton and Shipton. Another wood, called Skelton Spring, survived in Overton on the Shipton boundary until the 1950s (39 acres), as shown on the OS map for 1940.

The Abbot of St Mary's used Overton as his country retreat and kept the wood for his own use but, as none of his accounts survive, we know nothing of its medieval management. However, he did get his licence for the enclosure of Overton renewed in the reigns of Richard II and Henry VI (*Calendar of Patent Rolls,* 1908, p. 282). After the Dissolution the wood belonged first to the Crown, and whenever there was a change of tenant an effort was made to make sure that the wood was preserved. One enquiry in 1592 provided detailed evidence about the way the wood was being managed at the end of Queen Elizabeth's reign (Public Record Office: E134 34/35 Eliz.) In 1605 it was sold to the Scudamores and from the 1660s belonged to the Bourchier/Dawney estate at Beningborough. The estate papers do not survive so its later history is not known. It was certainly carefully preserved for game in the eighteenth and nineteenth centuries and an unusual yew plantation survives from this period. The Forestry Commission acquired it in 1959, covered it in conifers and have now sold it (Stapleton and Thompson, 1971: p.55). There is a little ancient woodland flora including dog's mercury *(Mercurialis perennis)*, an unusual plant in the Vale close to York. The internal banks and the sixteenth century records are of particular interest.

Beningborough and Newton on Ouse (Domesday woodland 3 × 1 furlongs /half league × 3 furlongs) had been given to St Leonard's Hospital in York, which had received various privileges from the king in the Forest of Galtres. These included various launds or thwaites which they used for hay and pasture and timber trees to build houses and burn for fuel, including fallen branches for charcoal (*Calendar of*

Charter Rolls, 1912, p. 454; Farrer, 1914, p.146). In 1452 this grant was withdrawn or exchanged for a grant of the Castle Mills in York but until then wood from the Forest of Galtres was used by the hospital including in 1379-80 when a man was paid 6*d.* a day for 67 days felling diverse oaks in the Forest and 2 at Sutton (Grange). These last were used to make thackbords and 30 great oaks were used for fuel. There was occasional income from bark (York Minster Library M2/(6c), f68v; York Minster Library M2/(6)b, f5). Woods in Newton and Beningborough are mentioned as boundaries in various charters and *c.* 1318-19 the hospital received a licence to enclose 56 acres of their wood and 100 acres of their demesne to make a park. The Inquisition concerning this described the wood as being a bowshot from the covert of the Forest with the king's highway in between but there was little use by wild animals save when the corn was sown next door! (Brown, 1898)[3]. The bank round part of this park does survive and does carry woodland species and woodland nearby still has dog's mercury. We know a little more about these woods from a visitation of 1377 and a few accounts rolls survive, with interesting detail particularly that 'fletes' or rafts of timber were floated from Beningborough to York and that in 1409 brothers went to Beningborough to supervise the carriage of timber to the River Ouse. In 1377 the Master of the Hospital had sold so much timber from the wood that the wood was nearly destroyed (Cullum, 1989), which may be why the park seems to have been a more important resource than the wood in the years for which accounts survive. For example, in 1460, faggots were sold in small quantities in 37 different lots, including 2 lots to Richard, Count of Warwick, the 'kingmaker' (York Minster Library M/2d.f54). But even with 1760 faggots made from rammis (decayed) oaks in the Forest in 1379-80 along with 3700 from the park at Beningborough, St Leonard's insatiable need for fuel had to be met elsewhere (York Minster Library M/2c.f72).

Land outside Forest Law
Outside the forest each township could have an enclosed wood but all the holders of land had rights to estovers ie. husbote, hedgebote, ploughbote, etc and usually to pasturage. The lords of the manor could charge for pannage, ie. for the pigs entering the wood to eat fallen acorns, but if a lord wanted a completely private wood he had to make some arrangement with the rest of the inhabitants.

Examples can be taken from woods for which later records survive. Escrick and Deighton, which were included with Langwith in the Domesday record of 2 × 2 leagues of woodland pasture, had been given to St Mary's Abbey by Alan, Earl of Brittany and Richmond and his tenant. Escrick was then granted to a Picot de Lascelles before 1161, though the Abbot and Convent reserved the right to keep 3 carts in the wood with 12 oxen, four for each cart, to take fuel and to take dead

---

[3] The road is now a minor one to Tollerton but was then an important route to the north.

wood timber everywhere they wished without impediment. They could also keep 140 pigs there without paying pannage (Clay, 1935). By 1226 the Abbot was complaining that he could not use his rights because of the sale Picot had made of the wood, so Picot agreed to grant the Abbot 130 acres of land and wood by the perch of 25ft with free way in and out between the road that leads from Scalewissbrigg (now Scorce bridge) towards Escrick, which is called Riccall gate, and between the bounds of Riccall and Kelfield, with liberty to enclose and do with as they will. Picot kept the rest of the woods though the abbot's tenant in Escrick could have common for 10 cattle and could take wood for building and for burning, as the other Escrick tenants did (Parker, 1923). In 1274 these woods appear in an enquiry about local roads, and in 1362 a bitter complaint was made that the King's Street between the Abbot's park and the wood of Ralph Lascelles had become choked with underwood and was dangerous. Despite disclaimers Ralph was told to keep it clear in future (Putnam, 1939; Flower, 1923). It is now the A19. The Abbot's park in Escrick was confusedly known as Riccall Park. It and Deighton woods continued in the possession of the Abbot of St Mary's until the Dissolution of the Monasteries. Timber for Bosses in the Minster came from Deighton in 1471 (Raine, 1859).

Deighton and Escrick feature in another type of documentary evidence: manorial documents. In the fifteenth century there were numerous prosecutions of men from Fulford and Deighton and other local villages for stealing wood and allowing their pigs to trespass (Yorkshire Archaeological Society DD88/1; Hull University DDBH 3/1; see also Bishop Wood 1347; West Yorkshire Archive Service, Leeds GC M3/1).

Surveys or extents of manors can sometimes show that transporting wood was a duty for villein tenants. For example, at Hambleton, villeins holding a bovate had to cart 5 loads of wood at Le Flete without food for the use of the granger at Selby and were paid 1½d. a load, value 5d. They also had to cart wood to the Abbot's hall in Selby and were given breakfast (Bishop, 1937). The service of carting wood was also due from the Archbishop's tenants at Cawood, Wistowe and Sherburn, and Riccall prebendal tenants had to cart wood for the lord's hearth and timber when he wished to build. At Dunnington they had to cart brushwood to York in return for a meal (West Yorkshire Archive Service, Leeds, Gascoigne Coll (GC): M3.210; Bishop, 1937, p.2) and at Alne and Tollerton the drengs had to carry timber to the Treasurer's houses in York and Alne "and had food". Bondmen, as well as carrying timber, had to fell 5 cartloads of underwood, carry it to Newton, stack it there, enclose it with a hedge and help load it on to the water (Lichfield Record Office: Ms.RR3).

Preserving a wood required a deliberate decision to keep animals out after the underwood was cut. If a wood was subject to pasturage it needed a strong landlord to enforce rules against custom or an agreement that each man should hold his own piece of wood. Monastic landlords, once free of the Forest laws, were particularly successful at 'persuading' their tenants to hand over their rights in the township wood. Selby Abbey, St Mary's Abbey and Fountains Abbey chartularies provide examples. As a result of this enclosure and 'privatisation' monastic woods became the prime source of timber in the latter part of the Middle Ages. The Fabric Rolls of York Minster, the Bursars Accounts of the Vicars Choral, and the accounts for rebuilding Ouse Bridge in 1527 show that timber and scaffold poles came from Deighton, Wollas & Poppleton (St Mary's), Hambleton & Acaster Selby (Selby), and Thorp Underwood (Fountains) as well as Nun Appleton, Nun Monkton, Marton and Healaugh (Figure 7.1). All the wood for Ralph de Hastings' engines also came from these woods. Some private landlords preserved their woods and provided timber for York buildings, notably the Percies at Topcliffe, Catton and Spofforth. Others at Aldwark, Cowthorp and Ingmanthorpe and Kexby also featured. At Elvington the tenants took control of their portion of wood and it gradually disappeared but the 'Lord's' wood survived and in the fifteenth century was providing regular crops of faggots, about 8000 per year, which were sold in York. The hedge was, as one might expect, repaired (Public Record Office: DL.29.105/11,12,13; E.101.484/2).

Two monastic landlords have left records that throw some light on woodland management: St Leonard's and Selby Abbey. At the woods of St Leonard's, at its Grange of Acomb and in Mossawe at Rufforth, the main product was fuel, which was produced in quantity. For example, in 1379-80 Roger Kydder and his men produced 31,600 faggots (York Minster Library: m2(6)c f19, f45). Another year, 75 cart-loads of timber were taken to the Ouse to be taken to York for building and repairing houses from Mossawe, the adjoining wood in Rufforth (York Minster Library: m2(6)c f28). Bark was sold and rushes harvested. Another product of the wood was piles or pynnes to repair staithes at Broomfleet and Morhamwyck. These were sent in wagons to the River Ouse at Bishopthorpe. They were then transported by water. During the years of the accounts far more timber went for the staithes than for building. There were regular payments for repairing the hedges and gates round the wood and for driving animals out of it. A 'haiator' was employed. The woods here survived the Dissolution of the Monasteries but were cleared in the eighteenth century. The last vestige in Rufforth was on the 1940 OS map and a scrap now houses air-raid shelters from the last war along with a few bluebells and wood anemones.

Despite a park and a managed wood, St Leonard's still had to buy in timber, particularly for its reconstruction of staithes. For example, it made a contract to fell woods in Nun Appleton and Moreby and sent its tenants from Heslington to do the carting from the latter wood to the river bank. Felling a wood by contract must have been one way of handling what was a major undertaking. Underwood seems to have been felled at between 12 and 18 years of age, so a managed wood might have several haggs or coppices which were felled in rotation. At Overton the 9 coppices ranged in size from 8-30 acres. The oldest coppice was called "Beningbrough Hagge, the springe wood of 12 yeres growth". The youngest was Bransby spring with spring wood of 1 year. The others ranged in between (Public Record Office: SC 12/22/93).

A contract to cut a coppice was occasionally entered in a monastic chartulary or register. At Sinningthwaite nunnery, the agreement was with Thomas Holme, a York merchant to cut all the trees, underwood and borders in one wood called Le Fall for 3 years. He could use the open field selion (strip) adjoining the wood to make charcoal but when he finished he was to remake the hedges and leave them in a proper state (Borthwick Institute of Historical Research: PH 104).

For Selby Abbey several contracts survive, recorded in memoranda books (Public Record Office: DL 42/8; West Yorkshire Archive Service: SA f72). They were with groups of local men and were for the West Hagg, East Hagg, North Hagg and Aughton Hagg at Hambleton in different years. They excluded oaks, maples and apples. The cutting could take place over a number of years, in the first case from 1355-59. The cutting was to be done in such a way that the regrowth would be protected. No cutting was to take place for a fortnight before and after the feast of St John the Baptist. In forests, this period was known as fence month and access was discouraged to protect the does and their newly born fawns. Here the main concern seems to have been to protect the 'spring'. Was this a period when growth was particularly rapid so more vulnerable than either earlier or later? Each parcel, when cut, was to be kept separate to protect the new growth, though the workmen could have space to cart from the wood to the pool (Selby Dam). They could use this 'Kirk Dike' to transport the wood to Selby but only during the daytime. At the end of the term they had to rebuild the banks of the coppice. At East Hagg, the conditions were similar though, there, they had to leave the underwood near the outer hedges, presumably to remake them. In North Hagg the contract was for a 4th part of the crop of underwood. No timber was to be taken and half of the underwood was to be left to the Abbot for his warden. The contractor could transport the wood on a boat but oxen from parts of Elmet could also enter the woods at a specially made gate. The use of the Selby Dam for transport is particularly interesting. It was also made use of by those who were felling wood in the archbishop's wood of Skaholme (Public Record Office: DL 42/8).[4]

The outlay for the purchase of one coppice was considerable. In 1431-2 one John de Esthorpe purchased the underwood of East Hagg, Hambleton for £66 13s. 4d. The Abbey then purchased back from him 300 astell for 6s. for the Abbot's sister, which were sent to Hull by boat! There were other gifts of astell to various monks and to a barber in York. The abbey also purchased back 500 sap lattes and

---

[4] Part is printed in *The Coucher Book of Selby Abbey II*, ed J. T. Fowler, Yorkshire Archaeological Society Record Series, vol. 13, p.382, as an appendix.

1000 stone lattes and a further 600 lattes for building the Abbot's chamber, as well as 400 for other buildings in the abbey. In the same year £17 6s. 8d. was received for oak saplings and underwood at Gunby. There, the felling and remaking the hedges were supervised by the Vicar. Fuel at the abbey included old oaks, turves and sea coal. Oaks were felled and converted into boards as well as more lattes. Long faggots and underwood were felled for repairing staithes (Hull University: DD LO 20/1).

So, the picture is similar to that for St Leonard's except that there are some contracts for felling coppices. An additional technical point is that men were specially paid for cutting 'virgul' withies for binding the faggots; cutting 3000 cost 16d. or 4 days' work. The emphasis is once again on fuel. Expenditure on this was a major item in the accounts; up to £18 a year where foreign expenses were £19 (Hull University: DD LO 20/6). Different coppices were cut each year. The records are too diffuse to be able to work out a sequence but all the coppices mentioned in later records were in active use in the fourteenth and fifteenth centuries. Sadly they have almost all now gone with the possible exception of Brayton Bargh.

Bishopwood, the largest block of woodland in the Vale, was related to the Archbishop's estate of Sherburn and the few documents show that it was never a township wood but was known as the Outwood of Sherburn. The Archbishop received an income from pannage and the value of customary works each tenant had to do, of carrying wood for one day. Forty-four holders of bovates of 'bond' land were still doing these services in the fifteenth century or paying 2d. each to avoid them. A forester was employed and provided with clothes. There was some income from selling underwood and bark and 15s. was spent on new making 209 perches of hedge round the woods of Skaholm and Pilehagg. These few accounts are from when the Archbishop's estates were in the king's hands, 1315-1318 (Public Record Office: SC6 1144/1, 1144/2. 1144/4). In 1388 an inquisition of Archbishop Neville's possessions showed stocks of firewood at each manor (*Calendar of Inquisitions Miscellaneous*, 1962, p.75, 80). Throughout the period there were gifts of timber from the Archbishop to St Leonard's Hospital and to York Minster. These sometimes mention parts of the wood. For example, in 1404 timber was sawn into boards in Scalm, in 1421 12 trees were given, chosen by the Minster carpenters, and in 1469 45 oaks. Most seem to have been taken to Cawood and then to York by boat before being sledded to the Minster. Archbishop Thoresby took sufficient interest when asked for timber for the nave ceiling to give instructions to cut timber in the winter season so that it would dry during the summer and be usable the following winter (Raine, 1859).

After the Dissolution of the Monasteries
We have seen that during the medieval period the woodlands of the Vale of York shrank in extent but what remained was more carefully managed to provide timber

for building, houses, churches, castles, mills and staithes. Underwood was cut for charcoal and for faggots and occasional trees for carts or barrels. Where there are records, as there are for St Leonard's hospital and Selby Abbey, they show that the most significant product was fuel, but they are few and scattered, until the time of the Dissolution of the Monasteries 1536-40, when the well-managed monastic woodlands providing a regular crop of fuel in the form of faggots or kyddes and timber for customers, who would go out to a wood and choose the tree they wanted, were recorded for that brief period when they were in the king's hands.

A suspicious monarch and a wheeler dealer official at the Court of Augmentations led to extra files being compiled for Yorkshire woodlands to try to prove that the official, Leonard Beckwith, had been abusing his position. A typical entry is that for Deighton spring, which "conteyns by estimate abowt the ryng 2 myles owt of which wood hath been taken since the dissolution towards repaire of newe paile of the park of Leconfield to the number of 1050 timber trees by Leonard Beckwith as also 19 tymber trees for repayre of the kings tenements in Fulford by assessment of John Herbert, deputy receivor. 7 tymbre trees for and towards repair of kings mills called castel mills by assessment of Leonard Beckwith so that there is lyttle or no tymbre remaining within the said spring but only diverse yong okes of the age of 60 yeres and in some places sett with old runted and croked okes. The underwood hassel of sundry ages." Riccal park had "many timbre trees and was throughly sett with fair yong okes of the age of 40-50 years. The underwood hazzel and alder trees and redy to be solde. 243 trees employed on pale of Leconfield Park, 5 trees upon kings palace in York." Brayton Bargh and the woods at Hamelton including the East Hagg, the North hagg, Awghton wood and West Hagg are all described with the tree species of the underwood, which varied from holly to birch, alder and sallow. Hamelton Haugh had been "well sett with yong okes". The underwood also of oak had been felled by Leonard Beckwith "at an unseasonable time wherof the said Spring is lyke to be utterly destroyed." This is quoted in more detail because it shows well the importance of preserving the spring "...Leonard Beckwith had commanded the kings stayth men in those parts with other work folks in the months of July and August to cut down and fell the wood being fully put forth and being at high pointe of leaf a good quantity wherof is dead and never like to recover nor to grow again as is thought by practical woodmen." The evidence continued with more about Selby dam. This is 200 years after the Selby contracts for felling the woods at Hambleton but the same issues were still pertinent. Leonard Beckwith had purchased the fishing in the dam and leased it out. He was using the king's "catch" (ketch) and boat on the dam for "timber, wood or kyddes as liketh him best". The king had coppices and springs at Hambleton near the dam "of which yearly there is a great number of fagots, pyles cut down for reparations .... all which might be carried down from the woods to the margin of the River Ouse in the kings own ketch upon the dammn at reasonable wages 20*d*. a katch loading according as ..is accustomed but he utterly refuseth so to do ...but doth compell and force the inhabitants of diverse & sundry townships to lead the said fagots and other wood in their carts and wayns through very dangerous passage & depe ways which is not only a very great destruction of many poor mens cattle also loss to the king as he pays three times so much money for the carriage of 1000 fagot woode or kydds by land as his highness ought to do on the said water" (Public Record Office: E315 429; see also E314 34/6, E314 63/92, E314 63/93).

The flood of material continues with another survey checking up on a royal official in 1552 (West Yorkshire Archive Service, Leeds: GC FO 2). The survey ranges widely but includes many Vale of York woods. Again, choosing already familiar woods, here are typical details. In 1546 10 lodes of firewood had been given from Deighton wood and park to John Redman, who lived at Fulford, 6 timber trees went to Heslington to repair the king's houses as well as 8 lodes of firewood and 4 lodes of Garsell (brushwood). In the same year 1000 fagots had been delivered to Fulford to repair staithes along with another 10 lodes of firewood and 20 timber trees to Heslington. In 1547 17 acres of underwood were sold to 3 different people and 10 timber trees went to repair the Castle Mills. In 1549 6 trees went to Huntington and 6 to Fulford to repair houses, 60 to Stamford Bridge to repair the mills and 20 to repair tenements in Clifton. Other woods provided kyddes. In Woodhouse springe (Sutton on Derwent) 30,000 kyddes fetched £25 net of wages.

These records show a major exploitation of the woodlands. The tenants were entitled to timber for repairs but the sheer scale of the operation obviously raised alarm bells as the return for Poppleton states "Delyvered ...to dyverse & sundry persons under color they are the kings tenants 272 tymber trees a great part have been sold away by the said parties that received them." A little like some modern 'privatisation' deals ! The woodlands would survive if they were looked after and the fences maintained but this did not always happen, as we have seen at Hambleton, and similarly at Riccall Park, Escrick, the jury said that the fences lay open for two years to the great loss of the king's woods.

Where the Crown leased out an estate, it tried to ensure that the woods were cared for, but gradually the estates were sold and the woods would be exploited by the new landlords. Their survival depended on whether the value of the product was sufficient to outweigh the value of alternative uses. Round York there were no blast furnaces demanding a regular supply of charcoal as there were at Follifoot and Rievaulx. Timber was still needed for building: Ouse Bridge was repaired in 1527 and again in 1564-66. In 1527 the timber came from monastic woods (York City Archives: C 83;5, f183-8). The accounts for 1565 and 1566 sadly do not survive and there are few mentions of building in Elizabeth's reign. In 1549 the city was so concerned about the shortage of fuel that they "agreyd for reformacon of wodd ...two honest and substaunceyall men shalbe appoynted to survay the spryngs nygh abowte this Citie within the space of viii myles to see wherin they ar mysused or cutte doune" ...commons agrieved by "the skarcytie of wodd or fewell, whereby the inhabitaunts of the said Citie shuld be relevyed ....notwithstandyng there are dyverse spryngs being within eight myles compas..... whiche in tymes past haith beyn a great releyf to the said Citie whiche ar now utterly dystroyd (Raine, 1946).[5] Fuel was, it seems, an increasing problem.

Some institutions continued as they had always done. At Bishopwood a deposition of around 1565 records that there were 5 haggs and that the rest of the woods were known as the outwoods; that the inhabitants of Cawood had had common of pasture for their cattle and pannage in all the outwoods and in the 5 separate haggs except in the 7 years after they had been felled (Hull University: DDBH 19/34). The Parliamentary Survey of 1649 records the same five haggs and lists the trees in each of which the larger number were decayed or decaying. The archbishop had recently impaled, imparked and ditched a large part of his haggs to keep his deer from destroying neighbouring crops but some tenants had disagreed and pulled down the pale in "these unnatural wars" so they again lay open for pasturage (Borthwick Institute of Historical Research: CC AB 8/5). The tenants at Cawood and Wistow were still bound to carry fuel to Cawood castle when the lord was in the country and still paid a swine tax (Boulter, 1882: p.49-50; Borthwick Institute of Historical Research: MD 112). Bishopwood had shrunk but despite this is still the largest block of woodland in the Vale of York. All the way through the timber was reserved by the lord. In the eighteenth century a customary delivery to Bishopthorpe was 26 loads of ash kidding for oven wood. It came by boat along with 8 loads of pea sticks! Timber was felled in quantity. In 1752 956 tons were felled and in 1753, 910 tons with a further 355 tons of ashwood. 1155 qtrs of bark were sold which with the tops fetched £97 6s. 6d. (Borthwick Institute of Historical Research: CC AB 7). Blocks were felled at a time so over the hundreds of years that it has been managed different parts of the wood have developed different characteristics according to when they were felled and how they were managed after felling. It it now a complete patchwork with patches of deciduous wood, oak and ash with an understorey of hazel and ancient woodland indicators mixed with patches of conifers. Pine seem to have been planted on areas that had become heathy. In 1917 almost all the wood was sold to the Yorkshire Pit Wood Association, 774 acres for £31,000 (Borthwick Institute of Historical Research: CC AB 10/CAW.84). It was presumably clear felled. This explains why there are so few old trees. On the southern edge, adjoining Scalm Park there is a substantial bank

---

[5] This was related to the lack of enforcement of the Statute, 35 Henry VIII c 17. This had enacted that 12 standels of oak were to be left in every acre and that coppice woods of less than 14 years should be protected after felling for at least 4 years. D.Pickering, ed. 1763, *Statutes at Large*, vol. V, From the 32 Henry VIII to 7 Edward VI: p. 366-70 (Cambridge).

and ditch and adjoining Rest Park, another is marked on the map called Keepers Walk. I have found no evidence of internal banks but it is quite difficult to work out where one is in the wood, and there is more to discover, perhaps the boundaries of the original haggs. It is now actively managed by the Forestry Commission under a lease from the Ecclesiastical Commissioners with good public access and such activities as fungus forays.

On the whole, the picture was a retreat of woodland, though at Kexby in 1616 the wood, trees and underwood growing upon one wood or spring called the Milne Field were sold by Anthonye Teyle of York for £120 (Hull University: DDFA 8/20). Was this a wood planted on an old open field or was it merely the regrowth of wood on what had been open field land? As far as I know, it is the earliest example in the Vale of land that had been returned to woodland. Certainly rigg and furrow exist in the wood today and have been surveyed and mapped by T C Booth of the Forestry Commission with interesting comments about the differential growth on the riggs and in the furrows (Booth, 1967).

There is more material on the later management and replanting of woods but this survey will conclude with a brief comment on the end of the Forest of Galtres. In the reign of James I it was described thus: "the soile and woode are wholly the kings save certain loads of firewood claimed by the inhabitants of Easingwold and Huby....The woode are for the most part pollard trees of oak. The soile from York to the covert of the Forest (whiche is 3 miles at least in bredth and more in length is verie hard and heathy ground without any woode at all. The inhabitants within the forest do clayme the feedings by metes and bounds except some places that are inclosed for the king for his game of deer" (Public Record Office: LR2 194 f 129). Sutton on Forest inhabitants could claim husbote and could take "certain burdens of windings for walles of our houses and stowers when they are in decay" (West Yorkshire Archive Service, Leeds: TN/GF Book of Presentments 1620). James I had tried to revive forest law as a money-raising device but the inhabitants wanted disafforestation. How Hill north of Easingwold was described as " the most beautiful and pleasant peece of all the forest, elevated with a spacious and easy assent to a hill coppiced with fare oaks and other trees remarkable in that part for comliness and maie compare with ainie ..forest in England for statliness and pleasure", but it was enclosed *c*. 1619-20 and the whole process of disafforestation was completed by 1630. This has led to a large set of records and some maps (Public Record Office: MR 355; MR 363; North Yorkshire County Record Office: ZDV, mic film 1282 fr 7770). One of these shows the centre of the forest with the area later called New Parks. It had been one of the areas inclosed for the king's deer and on the map was more wooded than most of the rest. Two of the Woodland History Group, decided to follow up a feature on this map called New Buildings for which some of the building accounts and brickmaking contracts survive. We followed a public footpath and the first thing we saw was a huge pollarded oak,

Plate 7.1 The Galtres Oak

which we felt must be a relic of the forest (Plate 7.1). We went on following a boundary described in a seventeenth century survey as "a winding and indenting sike". The hedge was full of field maple *(Acer campestre)* and a gap with a little bridge across the stream tempted us into what turned out to be a very narrow strip of woodland lying between the stream and a bank which more or less followed the boundary of one of the 'thwaites' granted or confirmed to St Leonard's Hospital by Edward III in 1338 *(Calendar of Charter Rolls*, 1912: p. 454). This is still a separate farm but the wood strip is owned by the farmer on the New Buildings side of the stream. We immediately began to spot indicator plants and to our amazement found herb Paris *(Paris quadrifolia)* and goldilocks *(Ranunculus auricomus)* as well as wood anemone and violet. This was a real thrill and alerted us to the fact that ancient woodland could survive in tiny pockets if shielded by banks and streams from clearance and by size from conifers. This scrap is too small to be in the Ancient Woodland Inventory.   Despite this discovery the group has been unable to find ancient woodland elsewhere within the area formerly covered by the Forest except in the places where there were woods enclosed by licence from the king during the Middle Ages. There are a few bluebells scattered in hedgerows but in general fewer indicators than outside the Forest. The empty landscape of widely scattered farms and an area called Bohemia after the Winter Queen are better reminders of the past than the vegetation.

This much abbreviated survey of the Vale of York leaves a feeling of how much has been lost and how much of that loss has been driven by 'market forces'. Woods only survive if their product has value. Institutions, which wanted timber and fuel, paid men to make secure hedges. Estate landlords wanted income from arable and if they planted trees, most wanted quicker growing conifers. Game preserves and fox hunting coverts, now politically incorrect, have saved some woodlands but woods in the Vale with a rich species mix are rare indeed and should be treasured for posterity.

References

Bishop, T. A. M. (ed) 1937 *Extent of Monk Fryston,* in Miscellanea IV, Yorkshire Archaeological Society Record Series, vol 94.

Bishop, T. A. M. (ed) 1937 Extents of Prebends, in Miscellanea IV Yorkshire Archaeological Society Record Series vol 94.

Bodleian Library *Tanner MS 150,* Borthwick Institute of Historical Research MF 26.

Borthwick Institute of Historical Research PH 104.

Borthwick Institute of Historical Research CC AB 7.

Borthwick Institute of Historical Research CC AB 8/5.

Borthwick Institute of Historical Research CC AB 10/CAW.84.

Booth, T. C. 1967 *Plantations on Medieval Rigg and Furr Strips* Forest Record 62, Forestry Commission, London: HMSO.

Boulter, W. Consitt 1882 *The Book of Remarks of William Storr of Scalm Park 1687-1731* Yorkshire Archaeological Journal vol 7.

Brown, W. (ed) 1892 *Yorkshire Inquisitions I,* Yorkshire Archaeological Society Record Series 12.

Brown, W. (ed) 1898 *Yorkshire Inquisitions II,* Yorkshire Archaeological Record Series 23.

Calendar of Charter Rolls 1912 *1-14 Edward III 1327-41,* vol IV.

Calendar of Inquisitions Miscellaneous 1962 vol 5, *11-15 Richard II.*

Calendar of Liberate Rolls 1959 *Henry III, 1251-60,* vol IV.

Calendar of Patent Rolls 1908 *Henry VI vol 4, 1441-46.*

Clay, C. T. (ed) 1935 *Early Yorkshire Charters, Honour of Richmond,* vol IV, Yorkshire Archaeological Record Series, Extra Series.

Close Rolls 1902 *Close Rolls of the Reign of Henry III preserved in the Public Record Office, 1227-3,* vol 1.

Close Rolls 1922 *Close Rolls of the Reign of Henry III preserved in the Public Record Office, 1247-51,* vol IV.

Close Rolls 1928 *Close Rolls of the Reign of Henry III preserved in the Public Record Office 1251-53*, vol VII.

Cullum, P. 1989 *Hospitals in Medieval Yorkshire* PhD thesis, Univ. of York.

Darby, H. C. and Maxwell, I. S. (eds) 1962 *The Domesday Geography of Northern England*, Cambridge.

Drake, F. 1736 *Eboracum*, London.

Dugdale, W. 1846 *Monasticon Anglicanum*, vol V, London.

English, B. (ed) 1996 *Yorkshire Hundred and Quo Warranto Rolls*, Yorkshire Archaeological Record Series 151.

Farrer, W. (ed) 1914 *Early Yorkshire Charters*, vol 1, vol IV.

Faull, M. and Stimson, M. (eds) 1986 *Domesday Book, Yorkshire*, vol. 1, 302c.

Flower, C. T. (ed) *1923 Public Works in Medieval Law vol II*, Selden Society, vol 40.

Greenway, D. E. (ed) 1972 *Charters of the Honour of Mowbray*, London.

Hardy, T. D. (ed) 1875 *Registrum Palatinum Dunelmense*, Rerum Brittanicorum Medii Aevi (Rolls Series 62) vol II, p. 1183-5; vol III, p. 534.

Hull University DDBH 3/1.

Hull University DDBH 19/34.

Hull University DD LO 20/1.

Hull University DD LO 20/6.

Hull University DDFA 8/20.

Le Patourel, H. E. J., Long, M. and Pickles, M. (eds) 1993 *Yorkshire Boundaries*. Leeds: Yorkshire Archaeological Society.

Lichfield Record Office Ms. RR 3, Borthwick Institute of Historical Research, PH 56.

North Yorkshire County Record Office, ZDV, mic film 1282 fr 7770.

Parker, J. (ed) 1923 *Yorkshire Fines, 1218-1231*, Yorkshire Archaeological Society Record Series vol 62.

Pipe Roll Society 1889 *The Great Roll of the Pipe for the thirteenth year of King Henry II, 1166-67*, vol 11.

Pipe Roll Society 1892 *The Great Roll of the Pipe for the thirteenth year of King Henry II, 1169-70*, vol 15.

Pipe Roll Society 1904 *The Great Roll of the Pipe for the twenty-second year of King Henry II, 1175-76*, vol 25.

Public Record Office E 101.484/2.

Public Record Office E 101.597.24.

Public Record Office E 101.501.13.

Public Record Office SC 12/22/93.

Public Record Office SC 6 1144/1, 1144/2, 1144/4.

Public Record Office E 134 34/35 Eliz. Mich. 27.

Public Record Office E 315 429, E 314 34/6, E 314 63/92, E 314 63/93.

Public Record Office DL 29.105/11, 12, 13.
Public Record Office DL 42/8.
Public Record Office LR2 194 f 129.
Public Record Office MR 355; MR 363.
Putnam, B. H. (ed) 1939 *Yorkshire Sessions of the Peace* Yorkshire Archaeological Record Series, vol 100.
Rackham, O. 1991 *Trees and Woodland in the British Landscape* Dent, London.
Raine, A. 1946 *York Civic Records vol 5,* Yorkshire Archaeological Society Record Series, 110.
Raine, J. (ed) 1859 *Fabric Rolls of York Minster* Surtees Society vol 35 (partly translated in L. F. Salzman, *Building in England* 1967, Oxford).
Stapleton, H. and Thompson, M. 1971 *Skelton Village*, York.
Stenton, D. M. (ed) 1925 *The Great Roll of the Pipe for the second year of King Richard I, 1190*. Pipe Roll Society, New Series, vol 1.
Stenton, D. M. (ed) 1940 *The Great Roll of the Pipe for the sixth year of the Reign of King John, 1204* Pipe Roll Society, New Series, vol 18.
Tillott, P. M. (ed) 1961 *City of York*, Victoria County History, London.
Warter Cartulary, Bodley Fairfax 9, Borthwick Institute of Historical Research MF 90 f 58.
West Yorkshire Archive Service, Leeds, Gascoigne Collection M3/1.
West Yorkshire Archive Service, Leeds, Gascoigne Collection M3.210.
West Yorkshire Archive Service, Leeds, Gascoigne Collection FO 2.
West Yorkshire Archive Service SA f 72.
West Yorkshire Archive Service, Leeds TN/GF Book of Presentments 1620.
York City Archives C 83;5, f183-8.
York Minster Library *Chamberlains Accounts* E 1/1-84, E 2/21-22.
York Minster Library M2/(6)c.
York Minster Library M2/(6)b.
York Minster Library M/2d.
York Minster Library M/2c.
Yorkshire Archaeological Society DD88/1.
Yorkshire Philosophical Society 1993 *Annual Report*.

Chapter 8

Losing one's head in Sherwood Forest: the dead wood resource of the ancient oaks

Charles Watkins and Christopher Lavers

Introduction

Until fairly recently, commercial foresters have tended to view dead wood, whether whole trees or branches, as a potential breeding ground for destructive insects and fungi. John Nisbet (1895) argued that "All dead branches and the *débris* of thinnings should in all cases be removed from woods and plantations, and should not under any pretext be allowed to lie upon the ground for any length of time.... All foresters... who wish to have the woods under their charge in a good state of health and as free from the ravages of insects as possible, should use every possible means to have all small poles, branches, and brushwood cleared away..." (pp. 337-338). This view remained the norm until the late 1970s when dead wood and trees were increasingly recognised as important habitats for a specialised fauna. Dead wood itself provides a growing medium for many fungi and habitat for invertebrates. Holes and hollows in dead branches and trees provide shelter and potential nesting sites for birds and bats and other mammals. Standard forestry practice now accepts the importance of retaining and managing dead wood as a nature conservation resource.

Now that dead wood is valued there is a need to assess the extent of the resource and how it should best be conserved and managed. Kirby *et al.* (1998) have made estimates of the amount of fallen dead wood in British woodland using line intercept sampling. Information was collated from about 70 stands and the amount of dead wood ranged from zero, for recently cut coppice, through to 60-140 cubic metres of dead wood per ha in stands which had been largely unmanaged for 70 years. They identified standing dead trees as an important form of dead wood, but noted that large dead trees of 40cm of more in diameter were rarely found "because most woods have been cut over at least once this century and most large timber removed." Dead trees were found to be important in native pinewood samples.

In another study, Green and Peterken (in press) studied variation in the amount of dead wood in woodlands of the lower Wye Valley. They found that in mature stands which had not been managed for around a hundred years, the volume of dead wood was comparable to that found in long-unmanaged stands in continental Europe and north-east America. They also found that large well-rotted logs were very rare. Kirby *et al.* (1998) argue that further work on assessing the dead wood resource of British forests should include the simple visual assessment of the frequency of large pieces of dead and decaying wood.

In this chapter we present results of a survey of the dead wood habitat associated with the ancient oaks of part of Sherwood Forest, Nottinghamshire. Most of the surviving ancient oaks are protected as part of the Birklands and Bilhaugh SSSI which is found just to the north of Edwinstowe (Figure 8.1). The authors of this chapter were contracted by English Nature in 1995-6 to make an inventory of the ancient oaks and assess the extent of dead wood habitat in the trees.

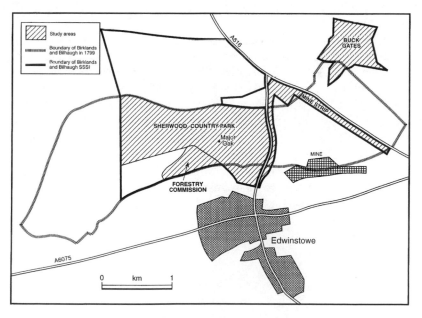

Fig 8.1 Location of the study area.

The ancient Sherwood oaks

In the medieval period Sherwood Forest covered large parts of central and northern Nottinghamshire. The forest consisted of unenclosed oak and birch woodland and heathland subject to grazing, and enclosed arable land and woodland. Some of the arable land was in the form of temporary enclosures known as 'brecks'. Most of the land was in private ownership, although large areas were subject to common grazing and other common rights until these rights were extinguished by enclosure. By the end of the seventeenth century the area of woodland in Sherwood had reached its lowest point (Mastoris and Groves, 1997; Watkins, 1998). Aristocratic landownership in the northern part of Sherwood Forest resulted in the area becoming known as the Dukeries in the late eighteenth century.

Many of the ancient trees were incorporated into parks. By the 1790s the largest surviving area of ancient oaks was at Birkland and Bilhaugh. The ancient oak trees were celebrated by local antiquaries such as Hayman Rooke (1799) for their great age and stature. They were protected by their new ducal owners throughout the late eighteenth, nineteenth and twentieth centuries. These owners valued them for their picturesque quality, their literary associations and for providing an ideal backcloth for country sports. The combination of medieval legend and trees old enough to have witnessed scenes depicted by Walter Scott was strong enough for the ancient oaks to become firmly fixed in the popular imagination as medieval icons (Watkins, 1998).

From the mid-nineteenth century onwards the Sherwood oaks became a popular tourist destination. Although the surviving parts of Birklands and Bilhaugh are only a few hundred hectares in extent, they have in recent years been recognised as of great nature conservation value and are an SSSI. The surviving ancient oaks are valued by nature conservationists for providing dead wood habitat and for their association with important fragments of lowland heathland. In addition to this ecological interest, the trees continue to be an important tourist attraction. The Sherwood Forest Visitor Centre, run by Nottinghamshire County Council, receives around one million visitors a year; the Forestry Commission has established a Sherwood Forest Initiative to help restore aspects of the Sherwood Forest landscape. However, the great age of the trees is probably still, for most visitors, their most valued feature. The most famous surviving tree is the Major Oak, which, using John White's method of dating, is currently thought to be over 1,100 years old (White, 1994).

Method
We were contracted by English Nature to use a method of survey which had been developed over a number of years by workers in Windsor Forest and elsewhere. A previous unpublished survey of Sherwood Forest Country Park had made use of the method in 1991. The aim was to nail an aluminium tag to every ancient oak within four carefully prescribed areas. The tags were numbered sequentially and it was intended that these numbers should assist long-term monitoring of the trees. The 1991 survey of the Sherwood Country Park area had used numbered blue plastic tags, but unfortunately many of these had subsequently been chewed and destroyed

by squirrels. Each tree was also to be marked on a map. However, trials of the method showed that this was very difficult to do accurately, so we marked individual trees on large scale aerial photographs instead. It was necessary to find and identify the ancient oaks before tagging them. They could normally be clearly distinguished from later generations of oaks by their size and form. Most of the survey work was done in the late winter and spring. This was important as the surveying would have been difficult to carry out when the trees were in leaf and bracken fronds would obscure fallen dead wood.

A standard paper proforma was used to collect the data for each tree in the field. Information was collected for 28 variables[1] including the category of tree, the state of the tree trunk and the number of live and dead branches. The results for these three groups of variables are discussed below. Standard definitions were provided by English Nature, but many of the variables were based on estimation rather than measurement and some apparently simple variables were in practice rather difficult to define. Branches, both dead and alive, were only counted if they were more than 15cm or more in diameter where they joined the main trunk. This width could be difficult to estimate for branches which were very high up, and care had to be taken when there was no clear single main trunk. The survey was carried out by the two authors assisted by three trained postgraduate students.

The inventory was carried out in the four areas at Sherwood shown in Figure 8.1, which superimposes the boundary of the modern SSSI on a plan of Birklands of the late eighteenth century (Rooke, 1799). Three areas were surveyed in spring 1995: Buck Gates (47 ha) which is maintained by the Thoresby estate as a reserve of ancient trees; a narrow strip of land used as a landscape screen bordering the colliery (39 ha), and a small area (15 ha) of land managed by the Forestry Commission. The ancient oaks of Sherwood Country Park (174 ha), leased by Nottinghamshire County Council, were surveyed in winter 1995 and spring 1996.

Tree categorisation

First we will consider the various categories of tree in terms of whether they were alive or dead, and whether they were standing trees, fallen or stumps. Each record in the database was classified into one of the following five categories 1: living tree; 2: fallen tree; 3: fallen trunk; 4: standing dead more than 1 metre in height; 5. stump (standing dead less than 1 metre in height) (Table 8.1).

---

[1] **List of 28 variables for which data were collected during the survey**
Tree number; Diameter at breast height (cm); Location type; Pollard; Whole fallen; Fallen trunk; Fallen limbs; Standing dead > 1m; Standing dead < 1m > 0.5m; Dead limbs attached total; Dead limbs attached with broken ends; Dead limbs attached with cut ends; Limb scars total; Limb scars hollow; Living limbs total; Living limbs with broken ends; Living limbs with cut ends; Visible heart rot; %Trunk bare of bark; Tree near path; Evidence of hollow trunk; Head of tree gone; Evidence of fire damage; Birch regeneration on stump or trunk; Other regeneration on stump or trunk; Bracken on stump or trunk; Evidence of animals; Coppiced tree.

The total number of trees surveyed in the four areas was 1577. Almost a thousand ancient oaks were catalogued in the Sherwood Forest Country Park (985, 62%). Most of the remainder were in the Buck Gates area (407, 26%). Smaller numbers were found in the small Forestry Commission (139, 9%) and mine (46, 3%) areas. By far the majority of the trees are, or were, standards. Very few of the trees could be classed as pollards (3 in total) or coppice (6 in total). There has not been a tradition of coppicing oak in Sherwood: the small number of multiple stems probably originate from regrowth from felled standards. Pollarding, however, may have taken place in the past. A survey of 1680 contains a rare reference to the cutting of oak branches: it ascribes the poor condition of 8,060 oak trees at Bilhagh to "oft lopping". This suggests that, in this section at least, pollarding was frequent, or had been so in the past. Although the residents of Edwinstowe retained a right to collect firewood in the late eighteenth century, it appears that pollarding had largely stopped by then (Watkins, 1998). There are now very few trees which show definite signs of having been pollarded within the last 200 years.

Table 8.1 General state of Sherwood Forest ancient oak population (all values %)

	Buck Gates	Country Park	Mine	Forestry Commission
n	407	985	46	139
Whole tree fallen	14	7	4	14
Trunk Fallen	1	9	30	1
Standing dead <1m	21	35	0	47
Standing dead >1m	3	5	43	0
Living	62	45	22	37

Perhaps the most astonishing finding of the survey is that over half (52%) of the total number of ancient oaks within the area studied were dead. In nature conservation terms this finding highlights the extensive dead wood resource which is to be found in Sherwood and the need for its careful management. The low proportion of live trees also indicates the need to consider how any natural regeneration of younger trees from the ancient oaks may best be conserved and encouraged. The proportion of dead and living trees varied considerably from site to site. The highest proportion living were at Buck Gates (62%). At the remaining three sites less than half the trees were living. In the Forestry Commission area 63% of the ancient oaks were dead, and in the small mine area this proportion was even higher.

There is a wide range of types of dead tree. Almost a third (31%) of all the ancient oaks were standing dead trees greater than 1 metre in height. These form an enormously important habitat providing a great quantity and wide variety of dead wood. They are particularly characteristic of the Country Park and Forestry

Commission areas. Kirby *et al.* (1998) note that in Britain standing dead trees with a diameter of larger than 40cm "are very rare indeed", but in Sherwood nearly all the standing dead trees are larger than this. The survey also identified 142 complete fallen trees, 103 fallen trunks and 84 large dead stumps less than a metre in height. Although the dead wood resource is very important for nature conservation reasons, those areas with a small proportion of living trees might well require particular attention in terms of the establishment of a new generation of oaks.

Trunk condition
Sherwood is famous for the size as well as the age of its ancient oaks. Our measurements of diameter at breast height (DBH) show that the mean diameter of those trees that could be measured (ie. excluding fallen trunks) varied from 118cm in the Forestry Commission area to 138cm at Buck Gates (Table 8.2). The relatively small mean DBH of 118cm of trees in the Forestry Commission area is possibly due to the large number of dead trees and the loss of bark through fire damage. Very few of the ancient oaks were below 50 cm or above 200 cm in diameter.

Table 8.2 Diameter at breast height (DBH) of Sherwood Forest ancient oaks

		Buck Gates	Country Park	Mine	Forestry Commission
DBH all fallen	n	49	38	2	15
	Mean	125	105	165	124
	Range	90-190	75-147	160-170	50-220
DBH dead<1m	n	73	310	0	67
	Mean	138	119		113
	Range	80-240	40-201		50-220
DBH dead>1m	n	221	428	9	46
	Mean	142	140	168	124
	Range	60-230	65-380	120-230	75-210

The survey results show that the great majority of trees have some evidence of heart rot and that most of the trees were hollow. The proportions given in Table 8.3 are highly likely to be underestimates as only those trees which had clear evidence of hollowness were recorded as such and in many cases it was impossible to discern whether this was the case. Estimates of the proportion of trunk bare of bark were generally easier to make, although they could not usually be made for fallen trees where the trunk was obscured by the ground or by vegetation. They show that the mean bark loss per tree was around 50% for trees at Buck Gates and in the Country Park, and as high as 79% in the Forestry Commission area. This is consistent with the large number of dead trees in that area.There is little variation in the mean number of limb scars per tree from site to site.

Table 8.3 Trunk condition of Sherwood Forest ancient oaks
(figures in parentheses are numbers of trees where measurement was possible)

	Buck Gates	Country Park	Mine	Forestry Commission
Mean DBH (cm)	138 (381)	129 (812)	148 (40)	118 (131)
Heart rot (%)	80 (396)	91 (932)	62 (26)	80 (139)
Hollow (%)	52 (396)	73 (932)	23 (26)	73 (139)
Head gone (%)	86 (337)	80 (783)	60 (10)	77 (118)
Bark loss (% of trunk)	50 (336)	59 (928)	16 (8)	79 (134)
Limb scars (per tree)	2.4 (337)	2.2 (783)	2.8 (10)	1.5 (118)
Fire damaged (%)	3 (407)	9 (985)	24 (46)	40 (139)

A characteristic feature of the ancient oaks at Sherwood is the large proportion which at some time in the past have lost their heads or crowns. Plate 8.1 shows such a tree which has clearly lost its top. The survey results show that a very high proportion of living trees and dead trees over a metre in height have lost their heads. This proportion is as high as 86% at Buck Gates and 80% at the Country Park. In most cases the damage clearly happened many years ago and the cause of this state of affairs is not known for certain. Historical records provide

Plate 8.1 A typical oak tree with a dead crown.

evidence of great damage to the oaks from specific storms. For example, the Accounts of the Surveyor General for 1716 show income of £850 from the "Sale of Trees blown down, broken and shattered, or otherwise damaged by a storm which happened on the 1st *February* 1714" (Anon., 1793, p. 504). It is possible, however, that trees of this great age always have a propensity to lose their heads.

Visible fire damage had occurred to trees at all sites. At Buck Gates where public access is very strictly controlled, only 2-3% of the trees had been affected by fire. The proportion was slightly higher in the Sherwood Country Park (9%) but was very much higher in the mine and Forestry Commission areas. In the latter as many as 40% of all trees had been fired. It is not known whether this high proportion is the result of many small fires, or one or two large fires. The lack of grazing and the resultant build up of dry vegetative matter means that there is a significant risk of fire at Sherwood. Developing adequate means of curtailing this risk, while at the same time not adversely affecting the quality of the dead wood habitat at Sherwood, must be one of the principal long-term management problems that remains to be solved.

Limbs
Further information on the extent and quality of dead wood habitat was collected by estimating the number of dead and live limbs (or branches) on every tree (Table 8.4). The number of fallen limbs found under each tree was also counted. The number of dead branches per tree varies from as many as 3.6 at Buck Gates and 3.1 in the Country Park, down to only 1.8 in the Forestry Commission area. Table 8.4 also shows the number of dead limbs per living tree. The number is again lowest (2.6) in the Forestry Commission area and high (4.4) at Buck Gates. When the percentage of limbs that are dead per living tree is considered, it is interesting to see that the highest percentages are at Buck Gates (51%) and the Forestry Commission area (47%) where around half of all limbs on even the living trees are dead.

Table 8.4 Limbs of Sherwood Forest ancient oaks

	Buck Gates	Country Park	Mine	Forestry Commission
Dead limbs per tree	3.6 (396)	3.1 (932)	1.9 (26)	1.8 (139)
Living limbs per tree	3.8 (252)	5.4 (439)	6.8 (10)	2.1 (52)
Dead limbs per living tree	4.4 (252)	3.3 (439)	5.0 (10)	2.6 (52)
%dead per living tree	51 (252)	36 (439)	40 (10)	47 (52)
Fallen limbs per tree	1.7 (396)	1.8 (932)	0.3 (26)	0.8 (139)

Very few limbs show evidence of having been sawn off. The area with the highest percentage of cut limbs is the Country Park. This reflects the need to protect members of the public from dangerous limbs. The Country Park (1.8), together with Buck Gates (1.7), also has the highest mean number of fallen limbs per tree. This large amount of fallen dead wood reflects the long-term non-intervention management policies at these sites. The small number of fallen dead limbs at the Forestry Commission and mine sites is probably a result of a combination of factors including past forestry management, uncontrolled public access and past fires.

Comparison of survey data in Sherwood Country Park 1991 and 1996

In addition to numbering the trees and estimating their current value as a dead wood resource, one of the aims of the research was to compare the survey results for the Country Park with a similar survey which took place in 1991. Overall the comparison confirms our view that measuring short-term changes in the characteristics of ancient trees is fraught with difficulties. One of the main problems was the inaccurate mapping of trees in the original survey. This made the relocation of individual trees difficult. This problem was compounded, moreover, by the destruction of many of the original blue plastic marker numbers by squirrels. Many of the trees had lost their tags altogether, others had been chewed to such an extent that the number was indecipherable. Our use of aerial photographs to map individual trees has solved this problem for future surveys.

Overall, the 1991 and 1996 surveys have 985 trees in common. The 1991 survey originally had 989 trees. The numbering sequence went up to 992, but tree numbers 23, 419 and 420 were missing. The 1996 survey numbering sequence had 997 trees. Five at the end of the database were new trees not indicated in the 1991 survey (993-997), 3 additional new trees were reallocated old numbers missing from the 1991 database (23, 419, 420) and 4 could not be relocated (104, 216, 556 and 611). The broad categorisation of trees is remarkably stable over the five year period. It appears that only five trees have died and this is not enough to change the overall proportions of 55% dead trees and 45% live trees in the Country Park.

It would also be useful to compare change in the other variables but, unfortunately, the relatively subjective assessment techniques make such a comparison invalid. For example, a superficial comparison shows that the mean DBH increases from 103 to 129 cm over the five year period. However, as there is an increase in mean DBH for both live and dead trees, the increase is clearly due to errors in measurement. One reason for errors in such a relatively simple measure is that the first surveyor measured the DBH without assistance, whereas in the second survey the measurement was made by a pair of surveyors working together. When each of us tried to measure DBH independently, we tended to estimate smaller diameters than when we worked together. This appears to be a simple consequence of trying to eye-up a large cylindrical object from a close distance with a long ruler. Clearly callipers will be required in future surveys.

To take another example, a comparison of the data from the two surveys suggests that there has been a decrease in the number of hollow trees from 875 to 684. This result can only be explained by different estimation techniques of the field surveyors. There appears to have been a decrease in the number of fired trees. It is possible that some trees with slight evidence of fire damage in 1991 no longer appeared fired in 1996, but it is surprising that this evidence has been lost from as many as 75 trees. Different surveying techniques may be a factor, but the evidence suggests that there has been no increase in fire damage over the five-year period.

Discussion
Overall the survey results confirm that there is a need to conserve existing dead and living ancient oaks throughout the SSSI. The survey has shown that the four survey areas have rather different management requirements.

Buck Gates
The survey has emphasised the importance of this area which has substantially more ancient oaks than was expected. The trees have a high mean diameter at breast height. This area has the highest proportion of living ancient oaks of the principal Sherwood sites. The long-term non-intervention policy of the landowners has resulted in a large number of fallen limbs. The area has the highest mean number of dead attached branches per tree and around half of all the limbs on even the living trees are dead. The strictly enforced policy of no public access has protected almost all the trees from fire damage. Little change in management is required at this site. In the longer term, a small pine plantation within the SSSI should be felled and consideration should be given to restoring heathland vegetation. In addition the possibility of reintroducing grazing could be examined. Public access should continue to be strictly controlled in order to reduce the risk of fire.

The mine strip
This narrow strip of woodland has few surviving ancient oaks. Some parts, such as Ollerton Assarts Plantation, have no oaks at all. The strip is very visible to passing motorists, however, and is therefore important in providing a superficial impression of Sherwood Forest. It also helps to hide the adjoining mine tip. Access is uncontrolled, and this has probably been a factor in reducing the quantity of dead wood habitat, and increasing the amount of fire damage. There is a considerable litter problem. We recommend that a management plan should be drawn up for this site. Consideration should be given to restoring heathland habitat, increasing the stock of oak and planning how to replace the maturing conifers at Ollerton Assarts Plantation.

Forestry Commission area
Almost two-thirds of the ancient oaks in this area are dead. In addition 40% of the trees have suffered from fire damage in the recent past. Although the trees provide an important dead wood resource, they have fewer attached dead branches than those in the other areas, and there are fewer fallen dead limbs. This is a result of past forest management. There is clearly a need to conserve the surviving ancient oaks and priority needs to be given to the encouragement of oak natural regeneration.

Sherwood Country Park
This area has the largest number of ancient oaks of the four areas at Sherwood. It also has by far the greatest amount of public access although this access is largely

restricted to paths. Just over half the entire stock of ancient oaks is dead. There is a high mean number of fallen branches. There is a smaller mean number of attached dead limbs than at Buck Gates and 70 cut limbs. This probably reflects removal of limbs in the interest of public safety. Almost 10% of the trees have been fired. Substantial plantings of oak were made in the 1970s. Most of the pressure from public access is concentrated near the visitor centre and the Major Oak. The comparison of the 1996 and 1991 surveys suggests that the population of ancient oaks has been stable with an average of one tree dying per year. It is recommended that management continues along current lines. Consideration should be given to the restoration of heathland vegetation where possible.

In addition to these specific conclusions, the study has shown that there are considerable problems in designing a foolproof method of monitoring change in the dead wood habitat even over a short period. The use of aerial photographs for the accurate mapping of trees was successful and should become standard practice. The main problems involve the difficulty of taking accurate measurements that can be compared over time and can be made consistently by different surveyors. Some sort of standardised photographic record for each tree is probably required. There is clearly room for much research on the historical geography, dendrochronology and genetics of the ancient Sherwood oaks to assist in the planning of practical management techniques for the control of bracken, the encouragement of heather and the establishment of new generations of Sherwood oaks.

Acknowledgements

We would like to thank English Nature for funding this research, Greg Smith for his help and guidance, Sallie-Anne Bailey, Hazel Powell and Deborah Worland for assisting us with the survey and the landowners and their tenants for allowing us to survey their woodland.

References

Anon. 1793 The Fourteenth Report of the Commissioners appointed to enquire into the State and Condition of the Woods, Forests and Land Revenues of the Crown, and to sell or alienate Fee Farm and other Unimprovable Rents, *House of Commons Journal* **48**, 467-511.

Green, P. and Peterken, G. F. in press Variation in the amount of dead wood in the woodlands of the lower Wye Valley, UK, in relation to the intensity of management, *Forest Ecology and Management*.

Kirby, K. J., Reid, C. M., Thomas, R. C. and Goldsmith, F. B. 1998 Estimates of the amount of fallen dead wood in British woodland making use of line intersect sampling, *Journal of Applied Ecology* (in press).

Mastoris, S. and Groves, S. (ed) 1997 Sherwood Forest in 1609. A Crown Survey by Richard Bankes, *Thoroton Society Record Series* Vol XL, Thoroton Society, Nottingham.

Nisbet, J. 1895 (ed) *The Forester* (by John Brown, 6th ed) Blackwood, Edinburgh, 2nd vol.

Peterken, G. F. 1996 *Natural woodland* CUP, Cambridge.

Rooke, H. 1799 *A Sketch of the Ancient and Present State of Sherwood Forest in the County of Nottingham* Tupman, Nottingham.

Watkins, C. 1998 "A solemn and gloomy umbrage": changing interpretations of the ancient oaks of Sherwood Forest, in C. Watkins (ed) *European woods and forests: studies in cultural history* CAB International, Wallingford, 93-113.

White, J. 1994 Estimating the age of large trees in Britain *Forestry Authority Research Information Note 250*, Forestry Commission, Edinburgh.

Chapter 9

Redesigning a region: The National Forest and quality of life

Morag Bell and Lois Child

Introduction

"Planting of trees in streets, in a sanitary point of view, cannot be overestimated. Besides exerting a beneficial influence in promoting improved habits, it awakens new thoughts and suggests fresh subjects for the mental exercise of the thousands who might otherwise be employed in the study of less desirable objects than those which nature provides and art cultivates. Trees not only afford shade and shelter, but adorn the landscape and purify the air. They improve the heart as well as the taste, they refresh the body and enlighten the spirit. And the more refined the taste is, the more exquisite is the gratification that may be enjoyed from every leaf-building tree" (Honorary Secretary, 1897).

"....trees enhance our lives and lift our spirits. They shelter our wildlife and temper our climate. They provide resources and employment....The planting of trees is a sign of our confidence in the future. It is a compliment paid by our generation to its successors and marks our gratitude to those who paid us that compliment in the past" (DoE/MAFF, 1995, p.118).

Despite the gap of almost a century these two statements share much in common. The first, by the Keeper of Victoria Park, Aberdeen, substantiates the advice which he gave to the Cockburn Association of Edinburgh during the 1880s on the Improvement of the city and its Neighbourhood. The second, from the White Paper *Rural England* published in 1995, forms part of the 'new' vision of the English countryside which it enshrines for the next century. Both emphasise the links between trees and human well-being. But far from a narrow physiological approach, they highlight the contribution which trees can make to an holistic interpretation of life quality through the mental stimulation, emotional fulfilment and ethical values which they promote. As Radley *et al.* (1997) point out, the topic of health should not be an adjunct to the study of illness and disease. Equally, the concept of health cannot be studied or discussed in isolation from the multiple spheres of life. It is integral to wider debates about society and the life of citizens including, for example, notions of suitable environmental and social relations. The nature of these relations is, however, the subject of much controversy. As many research studies demonstrate, questions of species mix, landscape design, cultural values and public access are important (Burgess, 1996; Kaplan and Kaplan, 1989). Gifford (1995) suggests that whilst over the last two decades environmental psychologists have explored person-nature transactions, this has focused primarily on architectural design and that the 'greening of psychology' is a relatively new field. This paper examines the contribution of the National Forest to these contemporary debates. It is divided into two sections. Firstly, we discuss the links between quality of life and environmental relations, and how, in the post-Rio era, visions of nature and citizenship implicit in the National Forest idea seek to promote a new relationship between nature, society and the state. Secondly, we consider the content of this 'progressive' vision and how ecology, aesthetics and ethics are deployed to give authority to it. In doing so, we outline some of the contradictions and tensions implicit in the Forest vision as the implementation process proceeds. Reference will be made to case study material taken from some key sites developed within the Forest since its inception.

Rehabilitation and transformation: creating a new landscape
The idea of creating a National Forest in the Midlands was proposed by the Countryside Commission 11 years ago in the policy document, *Forestry in the Countryside* (Countryside Commission, 1987). Unlike the earlier National Parks, it was to be an ambitious experiment to conserve but also to enhance, rehabilitate and regenerate the environment for the benefit of the nation. It was also to be unprecedented in geographical scale. The site finally selected in 1991 is a rectangular block of land in the East Midlands covering some 500 sq km (Figure 9.1). It extends into three counties, parts of south-west Derbyshire, north Staffordshire and Leicestershire. The objective is to increase tree cover from 6% to 30% in thirty years. A Forest Strategy was published in 1994 (Countryside Commission, 1994). It was followed in 1995 by the formation of the National Forest Company by the Secretary of State for the Environment and the Minister of Agriculture and charged with responsibility for implementing the Forest vision. Since April 1995 a series of planting programmes linked directly to the Forest have followed. These have made important if limited material changes to the landscape (National Forest Company, 1996). By contrast, the Forest as an idea and an ideal has been much discussed. It has entered a range of political, economic, scientific and popular debates on landscape design, citizenship and the health of the nation. One particular theme unifies these debates: the contribution of the Forest to an

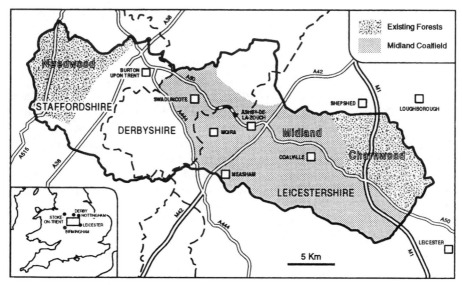

Fig 9.1 Location of The National Forest

improved quality of life. The broader context is twofold, namely, recent political and popular concerns in Britain over apparent social and environmental degeneration, and calls for a new relationship between society and nature in the post-Rio era.

Quality of life is a slippery concept. Its meaning, how to measure it, the political and social structures likely to deliver it, and how to assess it within and between countries, are the subject of much debate (Baldwin *et al.*, 1990; Nussbaum and Sen, 1993). The concept involves judgements about values in the human and natural world. It builds upon normative ideas and collective decisions on how individuals and societies ought to be able to live. In his wide-ranging analysis of the state of humanity, Julian Simon (1995) links the concept to a range of social, economic and environmental criteria deemed to be fundamental to a healthy society. That these should exclude prerequisites for material survival such as access to safe water, food and shelter, is generally agreed. In stating that "living comes before living well", Goodin (1992) asserts that the concept applies to human conditions beyond those deemed to be basic needs. He continues, "It makes little sense to worry about the quality of life before we are reasonably certain of life itself." Beyond the satisfaction of physiological needs, threats posed to human physical well-being from, for example, urban and industrial pollution, relate directly to life quality if not to human survival. Indeed, Perry (1993) notes that in developed countries the likely influence of climate change and global warming on quality of life is becoming a matter of increasing concern.

The concept relates not only to physical well-being but also to the moral, psychological and intellectual health of citizens. As Culyer (1990, p.21) points out, quality of life establishes connections between the characteristics of individuals and commodities, including their mental and emotional responses to them, and what they enable us to do. Central to this interpretation of quality of life is individual choice and the role of government in seeking to influence or restrict choice in the interests of the common good (Godfrey and Powell, 1990). Thus ethical concerns about nature, the degree of public participation in a revitalised local democracy and contributions to the democratisation of environmental knowledge may be interpreted as important dimensions of quality of life. Such themes have assumed global significance as a rise in popular ecological consciousness, the drive for greater political democracy and challenges to the power of western technocratic knowledge have become part of international discourse (Sachs, 1993). Linked to this broad interpretation of human well-being, quality of life enshrines both material and post-material concerns (Owens, 1994). It combines an expectation of rights and of obligations on the part of public and private sectors, voluntary groups and individuals. As defining features of the health and welfare of nations these rights and obligations are widely interpreted as fundamental to both national and international citizenship (Bulmer and Rees, 1996).

The National Forest initiative enshrines many of these principles. It is rooted in established scientific and aesthetic beliefs about the relations between human health and the physical environment whilst looking to the future in its attempt to offer something new. Indeed the Forest is about much more than planting trees. It reflects the recent redemptive qualities of trees and woodlands in landscape and cultural renewal. Since the sixteenth century, trees have provided a stabilising influence in English society during periods of accelerating social change (Thomas, 1983). They have been deployed to 'naturalise' different views of social order and to define the nature of landscape 'improvement' (Daniels, 1988). During Britain's imperial expansion, metropolitan knowledge of forest management played a key role in the export of 'progressive' environmental practices to the colonial territories (Bryant, 1996; Grove, 1995). This cultural hegemony notwithstanding, cross-cultural comparisons demonstrate the humane influence and aesthetic significance of trees in a long tradition of urban planning, architectural and landscape design. During the twentieth century, in response to the environmental destruction associated with unrestrained economic activity, the protection and expansion of forest environments has become an issue of national and international political significance. Since the formation of the Forestry Commission in 1919, policies have been directed to increasing the volume and productivity of trees across Britain. Recent world congresses on forestry have highlighted the threats to forest environments and the implications for forest management. Within many societies the loss not only of particular species but also the multiple uses of tree products, including their medicinal and nutritional properties, and the indigenous knowledge on which these uses are based, has necessitated adaptations and adjustments (McGregor, 1995; Moore and Vaughan, 1994). Popular protest and political sanctions (Wilson 1989) have been accompanied by detailed anthropological and ecological studies of hitherto little known social practices and unrecorded species (Gelfand *et al.*, 1985; Jahn, 1980; McGregor, 1991).

Two specific objectives which are central to the National Forest are highlighted here; its role in enhancing and regenerating the environment and in rehabilitating civil society. During the early 1990s both were identified by the Conservative Government as crucial to an improved quality of national life and were enshrined in the White Paper, *Rural England*. The former, it is argued, involves enhancing the environment through the production of a multi-purpose landscape. The latter emphasises that environmental values should be central to contemporary citizenship and that these values should be expressed through local democracy. The significance of the Forest does, however, extend beyond the national level. Within the context of contemporary global environmentalism, it has been linked with the discourse of sustainable development. Whilst pre-dating the Earth Summit, the National Forest concept was quickly incorporated into the UK response and has been referred to in a series of post-Rio White Papers including *Sustainable Development* (Cm 2426), *Biodiversity* (Cm 2428) and *Sustainable Forestry* (Cm 2429), published in January 1994.

Six principles central to Agenda 21 are enshrined in the Forest initiative (United Nations, 1992). Firstly, in its design and layout the National Forest has both a material and post-material rationale. It supports the view in Bruntland and the World Conservation Strategy that environmental protection and enhancement are not luxuries but basic needs providing the necessary conditions for health, survival and economic development. Secondly, it seeks to combat deforestation and to sustain the multiple roles and functions of forests and woodlands. Located in one of the least wooded countries in Europe, the National Forest not only seeks to promote tree planting but also the creation of a multi-purpose forest environment from which a range of public benefits will follow including the enhancement and creation of many wildlife habitats, the establishment of a major recreational and tourism resource, timber supply, stimulation of economic enterprise and employment (Countryside Commission, 1994). Thirdly, through the application of science to the planting process the conservation of biodiversity and the saving of endangered species are favoured. Fourthly, in challenging the mystique of inaccessible, technocratic science, the initiative aims to encourage the public understanding of 'green' science and to embrace alternative forms of knowledge through the promotion of public participation in the Forest's creation. Fifthly, the inclusionary nature of the initiative is emphasised. In reflecting Britain's late twentieth-century political culture that the state acts as facilitator and partner rather than sole provider of services, it aims to facilitate participation by and partnerships between local authorities, private enterprise and voluntary groups including women, children and youth. Sixthly, the initiative carries a strong moral message in seeking to encourage a change in lifestyles and patterns of consumption which are deemed to be essential to the achievement of sustainable development. In effect, it supports the concept not only of 'active' but also 'responsible citizenship'.

Thus, in reasserting the links between the health of the nation and environmental change, the National Forest provides a means by which to harness global principles to national needs. It emphasises that both material and post-material values are implicit in an improved quality of life. More particularly, it stresses that environmental enhancement not only underpins economic and social progress but that the process of enhancement itself may facilitate new environmental relations through the forms of knowledge and commitment to nature which it encourages and on which it depends.

From idealism to implementation
The East Midlands site was chosen in 1991 (Sheail, 1997). Within easy reach of most of the country's major conurbations, it was visually and economically mixed. Although bounded to west and east by the remnants of two ancient woodlands, Needwood and Charnwood, the area as a whole has a low level of tree cover; Leicestershire is the second least wooded county in England. In addition, north-west Leicestershire in the centre of the designated area is dominated by large tracts of derelict land and the workings of former coal mines. The area was therefore ideal to achieve the Commission's multiple goals. For this reason it was preferred over its leading competitors. In giving tangible expression to the Forest layout, the Forest vision builds on a modern tradition of landscape design which finds common ground with the work of Nan Fairbrother (1970) and Sir Geoffrey Jellicoe (1960;1966). It promotes an English woodland tradition and seeks to complement and enhance six distinctive Regional Character Areas across the Forest. These reflect the mosaic of land uses already within the designated area and are described as Needwood, Trent Valley, Mease Lowlands, Midland Coalfield, Calke Uplands, and Charnwood (Figure 9.2).

In 1991 the first trees in the National Forest were planted at Willesley Wood (Figure 9.3) by Sir George Young the then Minister of State for the Department of the Environment. Significantly, Sir George was pictured in publicity material planting an oak tree, making a strong statement that this was to be an English forest. The 40 hectare site at Willesley, under the ownership of the Woodland Trust, incorporates existing mature, broadleaved woodland, grassland, a section of the old Ashby Canal and a lake. Re-designed by the Trust with a view to both rehabilitating and enhancing the existing landscape, it has been planted with native broadleaved species, predominantly oak and ash. Through the skilful combination of a mosaic

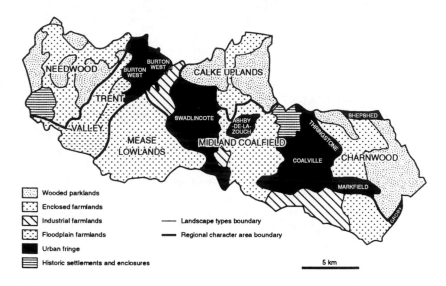

Fig 9.2 Regional Character Areas within The National Forest

of habitats a true forest aesthetic has been created which was formally acknowledged in 1996/97 when the site received a Forestry Authority Centre of Excellence Award. Implicit in the design of Willesley Wood is the assumption that the species chosen are appropriate for both the physical and human environment. One of the main features of the site, as with all Woodland Trust sites, is that the public are invited to walk in the woods and have free access. A comprehensive system of mown rides and footpaths connects the site with surrounding Rights of Way.

The initial success of Willesley Wood in combining an 'authentic' forest vision with improved public access, provided an optimistic launch to the National Forest. Progress with implementation will depend, however, on the planting of individual sites across all six Character Areas as they become available. The Midland Coalfield at the heart of the Forest, has been the focus of many of the schemes to date. This is due primarily to the availability of land and to the substantial range of funding opportunities available in the coalfield area. Derelict sites left as a legacy of coal mining have been acquired by local authorities in the area and restoration has been facilitated by financial support from public and private sources. These include European assistance through RECHAR, a group of European Community initiatives which draw upon the European Regional Development and Social funds for local economic development in Europe's Objective 2 regions, namely, older industrial regions which include former coal mining areas. Also included is national government support such as Derelict Land Grants through English Partnerships,

Single Regeneration Budget, assistance from the Rural Development Commission's Rural Development Area funding, private sponsorship from local mineral operators and the unique National Forest Tender Scheme.

As one of the first sites in the National Forest, Saltersford Valley Picnic Area (Figure 9.3) initially secured a high profile nationally as a pilot scheme. Located in the Midland Coalfield, it occupies a site where land rehabilitation is a high priority. Mining subsidence in the pasture land surrounding the Saltersford Brook had caused flooding and two large waterbodies or 'flashes' had been formed. The site was designated as derelict land and with the aid of a Derelict Land Grant, the local authority, Leicestershire County Council in collaboration with LandMark North West (a countryside initiative in north-west Leicestershire, supported by the County Council and Countryside Commission) designed this woodland, fishing lake and picnic area. Additional funding was provided by East Midlands Electricity and British Gas. The project raised the national profile of the National Forest in that the BBC TV Countryfile programme and Radio 1 donated a tree to be planted on this site for every entry they received in an environment competition. It is also a site

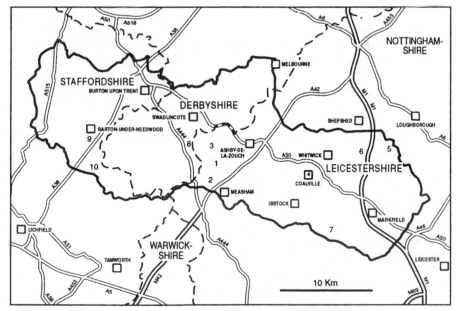

Fig 9.3 Site locations within The National Forest

Key:
1 Willesley Wood
2 Saltersford Valley Picnic Area
3 Sarah's Wood
4 Coalville Community Hospital Community Orchard
5 Beacon Hill Native Tree Collection

6 Charley Woods
7 Desford Lakes Demonstration Woodland
8 Church Gresley Demonstration Woodland
9 Barton-under-Needwood Demonstration Woodland
10 National Memorial Arboretum

which has benefited from strong, if carefully directed, local participation. In consultation with local residents two wooden sculptures, designed to reflect the nature of the site, were commissioned from a professional sculptor. Used extensively for recreation by the local community (the villages of Donisthorpe and Oakthorpe are close by), the site is overseen by a local warden whose responsibility it is to balance the demand for public access with the health of the physical environment in the form of nature conservation. His role is therefore one of policing as well as providing information to visitors. The site won one of the Forestry Authority's Centre of Exellence Awards in 1994 and its environmental value is now formally acknowledged through its designation by Leicestershire County Council as a Local Nature Reserve.

In spite of, or perhaps because of, the relatively slow pace of landscape change in many areas to date, the National Forest as an idea and ideal has been relatively uncontroversial. Indeed through active promotion of the project, not least from the regional press, its comprehensive overall design has secured widespread public support. But as implementation proceeds it cannot be assumed that harmony and consensus will necessarily be easily sustained. This is partly because the Forest vision/visions have within them the roots of tensions and conflict. These relate, in part, to the goal of achieving a multi-purpose Forest and the difficulties involved in reconciling 'competing' objectives. Balancing an enterprise culture with the conditions deemed to be important to human health represents a challenge, especially in areas where mineral extraction continues and there are proposals for new landfill sites. The Ashby Woulds area within the Midland Coalfield (Figure 9.3) contains a large number of mineral operators who continue to work sites for coal and clay extraction. The Ashby Woulds Forum, an informal consortium of the major landowners and parish councils in the area, was set up in 1991 when the East Midland location of the Forest was finally approved. The role of the Forum was to develop a strategy for restoring some of the worst degraded land. The strategy proposed a rehabilitation towards forestry and recreational use interspersed with business parks with a view to regenerating the local economy, which was suffering severely from mining closures. In order to satisfy this level of restoration, however, some of the voids created by mineral extraction have been put forward as landfill sites. In effect, landfill serves a dual role, as a repository for waste with an income through landfill charges and, when capped, a suitable surface for tree planting (Dobson and Moffat, 1993). Public opposition to continued dust and noise associated with this 'high level' restoration has led to planning applications being strongly rejected by the local community. Given that continued extraction of hard rock, sand and gravel, coal and clay play a key role in the future economy of the National Forest, this conflict will not easily be resolved.

Research on emotional responses to nature suggests that the beneficial effects of the latter can be linked directly to various forms of participation (Marcus and

Barnes, 1995). These include *viewing* natural scenes, *working* in a natural setting, the experience of *being* in a natural setting, and outdoor environments *chosen* by people as settings which contribute to reducing stress. Within the Midland Coalfield two sites reflect these direct and more positive relationships between human health and woodland. The first draws on the importance attached to trees in many cultures as a symbol of life. Entitled The Plant a Forest for Life campaign, it was inaugurated and spearheaded by Sir Cliff Richard on behalf of The Stars Organisation Supporting Action for people with Cerebral Palsy. A £5 donation to the fund resulted in half the proceeds being allocated to the provision of equipment for these children, and half to create a woodland which would be designed specifically for people, especially children, with special needs. The 60 hectare site (Figure 9.3), previously farmland within a derelict part of the Ashby Woulds area of the Forest, has been named Sarah's Wood after the young girl who appeared in the promotional material. Broadleaved woodland has been designed for wildlife and recreation around all-weather paths suitable for wheelchairs. A play area built specifically for children with disabilities and plans for a sheltered picnic area complement car parking with easy access for people with limited mobility. The second site highlights the therapeutic value attached to views, as opposed to the experience, of the natural world. Coalville Community Planting and Community Orchard is a small area of planting in the urban area at Coalville Community Hospital (Figure 9.3). The project was co-ordinated by LandMark NW and was supported by the National Forest, the Countryside Commission and by Leicestershire County Council. Broadleaved trees and shrubs including silver birch (*Betula pendula*), field maple (*Acer campestre*), oak (*Quercus* spp.), ash (*Fraxinus excelsior*) and hawthorn (*Crataegus monogyna*) have been planted to create a screen visible to patients from the hospital windows. Lord (1994) discusses the various benefits of views from hospital windows. A study in the United States concluded that post-operative hospital patients with views of trees from their windows recovered more quickly, required fewer drugs and had fewer complications than those looking out on to blank walls. In addition, to mark the fortieth anniversary of the Queen's accession to the throne, forty apple trees have been planted by the League of Friends of Coalville Hospital. The root stock for the trees was donated by H.P. Bulmer, the Somerset cider company. Two years after planting, old Leicestershire varieties of apples were grafted on to the root stock in order to preserve the old varieties for the future and to provide fruit to be used for patients in the hospital.

A central feature of the Forest is the emphasis placed on the conservation of native species and on biodiversity. Current scientific research favours the planting of stock of local provenance on the grounds that native species local to an area are better adapted for local environmental conditions; both abiotic, including underlying geology, soil type, climatic conditions, and biotic in terms of their resistance to disease. Native trees and shrubs also have an associated flora and fauna which is far greater in numbers and diversity than non-native species. For example, there are over 400 species associated with native trees such as pedunculate oak *(Quercus robur)* and willows *(Salix* spp) compared to about 50 species for sycamore *(Acer pseudoplatanus)* (Tait *et al.*, 1988). The Native Tree Collection at Beacon Hill country park (Figure 9.3) is designed to encourage this practice. However, the collection of local seed does not automatically bestow local native status. A project in Leicestershire being carried out by the National Forest, Charnwood Wildlife project and Leicestershire County Council and directed at growing trees from local seed, has found that even on a local Site of Special Scientific Interest mature trees were originally from Dutch stock (Evans, *pers. comm.*). Whilst the National Forest Company are working towards planting trees of local provenance, the ambitious targets laid down in the Strategy have as their objective 70% of total planting within the first ten years. These targets cannot be met at present by using native species with the result that large numbers of trees are being imported. There is, in effect, a conflict of objectives between idealism and the practicalities of achieving a noticeably established forest in a short period of time.

Pressure to achieve a 'forested landscape' has implications for other habitat creation and restoration schemes. The National Forest Strategy recommends a mosaic of habitat types which is characteristic of an English forest aesthetic. In Leicestershire this includes heathland. Whilst it has suffered heavy losses in the past due to agricultural encroachment it is acknowledged to be a valuable resource in the Forest Strategy. Where grants are available to plant trees and the incentive is great to give the National Forest a visual credibility, the threat to this and other habitats is considerable. Notwithstanding these real concerns, two sites, a Leicestershire and Rutland Wildlife Trust site at Charley Woods (Figure 9.3), and a site at Beacon Hill Country Park (Figure 9.3), are currently benefiting from their location within the National Forest boundary. At Charley Woods existing heathland on a large rocky outcrop is being managed to conserve a typical heathland flora including heath bedstraw *(Galium saxatile)* and climbing corydalis *(Corydalis claviculata)*. At Beacon Hill, a 1 ha area has been cleared of bracken *(Pteridium aquilinum)* with the aim of restoring the site to lowland heath. The site will be actively managed and the site area may well be extended in future, contributing to an increase in both habitat and species diversity.

Notwithstanding the emphasis on participation and local knowledge in National Forest rhetoric, the Forest also provides a setting for scientific trials and experiment, and for the communication of 'improvements' in planting design and practice to a broader public. Three Forestry Authority demonstration woodlands are currently located across the Forest (Figure 9.3). These sites have been established in collaboration with the Department of the Environment to demonstrate the various planting methods available to potential Forest site owners and also to provide valuable research into establishment rates of trees on three soil types (Kerr, in press). The first at Desford lakes, is planted on coal spoil, the second at Church Gresley is planted on low grade grassland and the third site at Barton under Needwood is planted on productive good quality (grade 2 and 3A) agricultural land. A number of trials are under way, some repeated at all three sites, including establishing new native woodlands (Natural Vegetation Classification W10, predominantly oak and birch), establishing oak high forest using nurse crops, natural colonisation (adjacent to existing woodland), comparing the relative growth rate of native vs non-native species, effects of tree spacing on tree growth and woodland characteristics, short rotation coppice and ground preparation techniques. These trials are intended to act not only as a demonstration to local landowners of what is possible on different land types but also to provide research data on new ways of planting and establishment with implications beyond the Forest boundaries.

Whilst ecological research within the Forest may have long-term significance beyond the designated area, and the emphasis in much promotional material continues to be on creating a 'national' landscape, questions remain over the ability of the Forest to retain a distinctive quality; one which is different from community forests. It does not achieve this in terms of size. Moreover, evidence suggests that hitherto the outward-looking appeal of the Forest has primarily addressed a sophisticated audience beyond the Forest area. For the majority of local people their major interests in the Forest lie in its ability to rejuvenate an area of mining decline, to improve the physical environment and to generate employment. One site currently being developed within the Forest may, however, have wider symbolic importance in its representation of quality of life. It is the National Memorial Arboretum in the Trent Valley (Figure 9.3). Planned by Forest Enterprise and developed by a professional landscape design company for the World Memorial Fund for Disaster Relief it is intended as a living memorial to those who have lost their lives in conflict (National Memorial Arboretum Appeal, no date). The site has been gifted by Redland Aggregates and adjoins a wetland Site of Special Scientific Interest currently managed by Staffordshire Wildlife Trust as a breeding ground for birds. The sensitivity of this site will be protected by a belt of informally planted native trees and shrubs which will frame the more formal design of the gardens. Central to the layout and species mix of the Arboretum is that it should combine a collective memory of the past with a vision of hope for the future which transcends institutionalised boundaries. The main axis of the site will be formed by a Millennium Avenue of lime which will be planted using clones propagated from a 2,000 year old tree from Westonbirt arboretum. There will be a memorial planting for the 186 countries of the United Nations, formal planting to commemorate those vessels lost to enemy action by the Merchant Navy, a war widows' rose garden, and a garden of the innocents commemorating the lives of children lost in conflicts around the world. Equally, in looking to the future, it is intended that the Arboretum will be associated with other arboreta and botanic gardens throughout the world in promoting the conservation and enhancement of species diversity across national and cultural boundaries.

Conclusions

That quality of life comprises an assemblage of a myriad of ideals has been established. As a new landscape for the next millennium, the National Forest enshrines many of these ideals. Its goals are nevertheless ambitious. In seeking to transform the environmental aesthetics and social well-being of a region by creating a multi-purpose Forest, conflicts of interest arise. As the case studies demonstrate, some of these conflicts are of national if not global concern. The extraction of minerals will continue to be undertaken throughout the Forest area in the foreseeable future. Whilst these are economically important activities in providing valuable local employment, the immediate effects of extraction in terms of dust, noise and nuisance are a source of tension and dispute. In the longer term, however, continued mineral extraction will provide opportunities for restoration to forestry. Indeed, in an area dominated by private land ownership where planting depends upon voluntary agreement, rehabilitation of worked land will remain a key source of sites for Forest planting.

Hitherto the Forest has been slow to materialise. New planting programmes approved since 1991 cover some 4,000 hectares but this is still well short of the target of 11,000 hectares in the first 10 years. A reluctance among many private landowners to convert even marginal argricultural land to woodland cover and to permit public access reduces the speed of tree planting required. The latest round of Forest Tender Scheme Awards announced in October 1997 will nevertheless contribute a further 217 ha of land to the Forest (400,000 trees) and, significantly, half of the successful bids were submitted by farmers. Notwithstanding the slow pace of landscape change, Forest rhetoric fits within many current debates on new lives and new landscapes. As a late-twentieth-century initiative, its novelty lies partly in its representation. The Forest itself is presented as different. It is seen as an experiment in landscape change which is conceptually different from its predecessors. In the post-Rio era it incorporates an economic, environmental and social agenda into quality of life on an unprecedented scale. Flexibility in detail, regional identity within a global context, environmental ethics and popular participation in both the production and consumption of the Forest are all important features of the design. Sites which have been implemented to date show an emerging forest of trees and other habitats. Several of these sites also demonstrate that whilst quality of life extends well beyond a green agenda, it is nevertheless an important means of mobilising people. Planting to date also indicates, however, that the nature of popular participation varies widely and that apathy in many areas cannot be related solely to passive citizenship. The aesthetics of landscape change form only a small part of often competing local priorities and needs. As sites become more mature, questions arise over the extent to which the visual appearance and experience of a forested landscape will create the kind of forest culture in which, as our opening quotations imply, trees become valued for their holistic contribution to human well-being and quality of life.

Acknowledgements

This paper draws on the findings of a research award from the Economic and Social Research Council under the Global Environmental Change Programme (L320223004).

References

Baldwin, S., Godfrey, C. and Propper, C. (eds) 1990 *Quality of life: perspectives and policies*. Routledge.

Bulmer, M. and Rees, A. 1996 *Citizenship today: the contemporary relevance of T.H. Marshall*. UCL Press.

Burgess, J. 1996 Focusing on fear: the use of focus groups in a project for the Community Forest Unit, Countryside Commission. *Area* **28**, pp.130-135.

Bryant, R. 1996 Romancing colonial forestry: the discourse of 'forestry as progress' in British Burma. *The Geographical Journal*, **162**, pp.169-178.

Countryside Commission 1987 Forestry in the countryside. Countryside Commission.

Countryside Commission 1994 *The National Forest. The strategy: the Forest vision*. Countryside Commission.

Culyer, A. 1990 Commodities, characteristics of commodities, characteristics of people, utilities and the quality of life. In Baldwin, S., Godfrey, C. and Propper, C. (eds) 1990 *Quality of life: perspectives and policies*. Routledge, pp.9-27.

Daniels, S. 1988 The political iconography of woodland in later Georgian England. In Cosgrove, D. and Daniels, S. (eds) *The iconography of landscape*. CUP, pp.43-82.

Dobson, M.C. and Moffat, A.J. 1993 *The potential for woodland establishment on landfill sites*. HMSO, London.

DoE/MAFF, 1995 *Rural England, a nation committed to a living countryside*, Cm 3016.

Fairbrother, N. 1970 *New lives, new landscapes*. The Architectural Press, London.

Gelfand, M., Mavi, S., Drummond, R., and Ndemera, E. 1985 *The traditional medical practitioner in Zimbabwe*. Mambo.

Gifford, R. 1995 Natural psychology: an introduction. *Journal of Environmental Psychology* **15**, pp.167-168.

Godfrey, C. and Powell, M. 1990 The relationship between individual choice and government policy in the decision to consume hazardous goods. In Baldwin, S., Godfrey, C. and Propper, C. (eds) 1990 *Quality of life: perspectives and policies.* Routledge, pp.201-217.

Goodin, R. 1992 *Green political theory.* Polity Press.

Grove, R. 1995 Imperialism and the discourse of desiccation: the institutionalisation of global environmental concerns and the role of the Royal Geographical Society, 1860-1880. In Bell, M., Butlin, R.A., and Heffernan, M.J. (eds) *Geography and imperialism 1820-1940.* MUP, pp.36-52.

Honorary Secretary 1897 *The Cockburn Association. A short account of its objects and its work.* The Edinburgh Press.

Jahn, S. 1980 *Traditional water purification in tropical developing countries.* German Agency for Technical Cooperation.

Jellicoe, G.A. 1960 and 1966 *Studies in landscape design. Vol.1 and 2.* Oxford University Press.

Kaplan, R. and Kaplan, S. 1989 *The experience of nature. A psychological perspective.* CUP.

Kerr, G. (in press) Establishing new woodlands: research and demonstration in The National Forest. *East Midland Geographer* **20** (1).

Lord, D.N. 1994 *Calling in the country: ecology, parks and human need.* Working Paper 4, The Future of urban parks and open spaces series. Comedia in association with Demos.

Marcus, C. and Barnes, M. 1995 *Gardens in health care facilities: uses, therapeutic benefits and design recommendations.* The Center for Health Design, University of California.

McGregor, J. 1991 Ecology, policy and ideology: an historical study of woodland use and change in Zimbabwe's communal areas. Unpublished PhD thesis, Loughborough University, UK.

McGregor, J. 1995 Gathered produce in Zimbabwe's communal areas: changing resource availability and use. *Ecology of Food and Nutrition,* **33,** pp.163-193.

Moore, H. and Vaughan, M. 1994 *Cutting down trees: gender, nutrition and agricultural change in the Northern Province of Zambia, 1890-1990.* Heinemann.

National Forest Company 1996 *The National Forest. A forest for all.* The National Forest.

National Memorial Arboretum Appeal (no date) Promotional literature

Nussbaum, M. and Sen, A. (eds) 1993 *The quality of life.* Clarendon.

Owens, S. 1994 Land, limits and sustainability: a conceptual framework and some dilemmas for the planning system. *Trans. Inst. Br. Geogr.* **19** pp.439-456.

Perry, A. 1993 Climate, greenhouse warming and the quality of life. *Progress in Human Geography* **17,** pp.354-358.

Radley, A., Lupton, D. and Ritter, C. 1997 Editorial. Health: an invitation and introduction. *Health* **1,** pp.5-21.

Sachs, W. 1993 *Global ecology. A new arena of political conflict*. Zed.

Sheail, J. 1997 The National Forest. From idea to achievement. *Town Planning Review* **68**, pp.305-323.

Simon, J. (ed) 1995 *The state of humanity*. Blackwell.

Tait, J., Lane, A. and Carr, S. (1988) Practical conservation. The Open University, Milton Keynes.

Thomas, K. 1983 *Man and the natural world: changing attitudes in England 1500-1800*. Allen Lane, London.

United Nations 1992 *Agenda 21, Rio Declaration Forest principles*. United Nations.

Wilson, K. 1989 Trees in fields in Southern Zimbabwe. *Journal of Southern African Studies*, **15**, pp.369-383.

Chapter 10

Woodland in the Landscape

Simon Bell

Introduction

Previous chapters in this book have considered the history of woodland in Britain, its decline, disappearance and neglect over many years. The present state of woodland conservation has also been reviewed. Recent replanting initiatives and the expansion of new woodlands close to communities and on redundant agricultural land have also been explored. Policies for expanding woodland and the justification for spending taxpayers' money for this purpose hinge on the perceived public benefits of landscape enhancement, improvement of nature conservation or provision of recreation facilities, as well as strategic goals such as reducing agricultural output or increasing production of timber.

New woodlands planted under the Woodland Grant Scheme and Farm Woodland Premium Scheme (a joint arrangement between the Forestry Commission and Ministry of Agriculture, Fisheries and Food) must meet certain conditions in order to attract grant aid. Amongst these is adherence to landscape design principles set out in documents such as the 'Lowland Landscape Design Guidelines' (Forestry Commission, 1992). The principles contained in these guidelines were developed by technical experts from more general landscape architectural models and applied to forest and woodland design. This strategy appears, on the face of it, to have been successful but only recently are these empirically developed principles undergoing a degree of checking and calibration. By studying the perceptual and aesthetic responses of members of the public, for whose benefit the new woodlands are being created, it should be possible to check whether the experts' *a priori* expectations of preferences are borne out. At the heart of such studies lies the issue of people's relationships with woodlands as part of the landscape rather than as features or elements in their own right.

People and Woods: the cultural context

We now know that woodland clearance commenced during the Neolithic period and progressed at such a rate that large areas of the country developed a predominantly open character by Roman times and have remained that way ever since. Thus the experience and perception of woodlands which has become embedded in British culture is quite different from that found in other countries. Even the words 'forest' and 'wood' appear to mean quite different things and to embody certain associations and symbolism which can complicate our efforts at understanding public preferences and perceptions.

The term *forest* originally referred to a hunting ground for kings and aristocracy comprising a semi-natural, uninhabited area usually including woodland, wood pasture, heath, bog and other vegetation. Associations with Norman kings, dispossessed Saxon peasants, outlaws and wildness persist to this day. However, the word is also associated by many people with modern plantation forestry of introduced conifer plantations of even-aged monocultures. Thus, when we ask people what they understand by the term forest we get mixed replies. Some view forests in a negative light (the "serried ranks of alien conifers", dark, forbidding and lacking wildlife) so that the use of the term applied to 'Community Forests' or the 'National Forest' can produce misconceptions as to what these new wooded landscapes will be like.

The words *wood* or *woodland* by contrast, conjure up other associations: of small, mainly broadleaved and managed patches of trees set amongst farmland. The presence of old trees seems to be significant. Respondents to one of the surveys discussed below, considered that in order for a group of trees to become a 'wood', the trees needed to be quite old and big enough to have a clear space beneath them. It also seems that most people do not think of woods as separate from the landscape as a whole. Whilst an individual landowner may think of his own land and the management of a single wood within it, the general public, whilst they recognise that the land is privately owned, do not see an ownership pattern but a landscape whose boundaries are perceptual, not legal or administrative.

Foresters, farmers and other land managers tend to view woodlands differently from the general public. Farmers have been historically engaged in woodland clearance in order to create farmland. The areas of woodland left behind as they did so were kept to fulfil a useful purpose or were sited on inaccessible or useless terrain. The tamed, comfortable landscape created by farmers is the antithesis of the wild, untamed, unruly forest. Scientific forestry management started in the seventeenth century during the Age of Enlightenment and was only applied in Britain in the nineteenth and particularly the twentieth centuries. Thus the foresters' taming of the remaining woodlands and their conversion or reafforestation into tidy compartments of straight-stemmed trees along rational, Cartesian lines has around 100 years of history. This is long enough for associations with such layouts to be accumulated and become somewhat embedded in the British culture.

Against this background research has tried to elucidate several aspects.

1. During the late 1980s and early 1990s research was carried out that aimed to find out what kind of forest or woodland landscapes were preferred by the public and to try to link this with design principles.
2. Recent research into the landscape value of farm woods that attempts to calibrate design principles contained in guidelines.
3. Research into perceptions of fear and safety experienced by visitors to woodlands, especially around towns.
4. Aesthetic research into the psychological effects of being in woodland or the values of trees and woods in our everyday lives.
5. The benefit or value attached to making improvements in forests and woodlands.

Each of these areas will be reviewed.

1. Forests, Woods and People's Preferences

In the late 1980s, Lee undertook a research project co-funded by the Forestry Commission, Countryside Commission and the then Countryside Commission for Scotland (Lee, in press). The research pursued a 'psycho-physical' approach where a single aspect such as scenic quality is related to relatively objective physical features of the environment. In this way the preferences expressed in terms of good or bad scenic quality can be correlated to the application of design principles.

This research had several components:

- Focus groups
- Expert seminars
- Household survey
- Landscape Preference Study

The focus groups were used as a means of developing the content of the Household Survey questionnaire. The groups, held in different parts of the country, discussed their knowledge, use, feelings and attitudes to the countryside, forests and woods.

The two expert seminars were used as a means of obtaining the views of people with a special interest in forests, the countryside and their management. The groups were able to 'brainstorm' the issues from the focus groups and help to develop the questionnaire for the Household Survey.

The Household Survey was used to provide information on the ways in which forests are perceived by the public, the extent and types of forest use, current attitudes towards design and management and public perceptions of the aesthetic aspects of forest and woodland landscapes. They took place in four areas and whilst not specifically selected to be socially representative of the British population they were in fact close to being so. The survey included a landscape preference question where respondents were shown distant landscape photographs and asked to rank them in order of preference.

The Landscape Preference Study aimed to explore people's preferences for landscape presented visually. It departed from previous studies that had tried to elicit preferences for the purely perceptual (and some would say essentially aesthetic) qualities of a scene and instead endeavoured to test preferences for different landscapes when viewed with a purpose in mind. This relates to the affordance theory of perception advanced by James J Gibson (Gibson, 1979) who contends that we perceive landscapes in terms of what they afford us. Thus if we plan to go for a walk we look at the landscape in a different way from if we are seeking a good place to go hunting, for example.

As well as the purpose for which we are viewing the landscape, different preferences might be expected from different people, perhaps on the basis of sex, age, and degree of education. This information is easily obtained during a survey. Finally, it was considered important to try to link some of the physical properties of the scenes with the preferences expressed for them so that the research findings could be applied to design and management. The judgement of the 'experts', that is the then team of Forestry Commission landscape architects, would then evaluate the same scenes in terms of how 'good' their design was, measured in terms of their fulfilment of the design principles used in forest design (Forestry Commission, 1989). Such an ambitious project required a lot of data so as to be able to subdivide it into different categories and still have sufficient samples for analysis. Several sub-sets of photographs were used, including distant and close scenes.

The subjects who took part were drawn from those actually visiting forests, interviewed at Forestry Commission visitor centres. A rating board was used to lay out the sample photographs in a spatial pattern for comparative ranking (an important feature because people are good at making relative judgements but not so good at absolutes). The photos were ranked in terms of how good or poor they were felt to be for the purpose (having a picnic, going for a walk, producing timber, etc) given at the start of each session.

The landscape architects evaluated each scene against a scale of 1-5 (good to poor) in terms of how well they met the design principles deemed to produce attractive landscapes, such as scale, shape, species proportions, overall diversity, species, colour and age diversity, density, human intrusion and *genius loci*. Some are obvious physical attributes (for example shape), others primarily aesthetic (*genius loci* or spirit of place).

This research yielded some very useful results. The Household Survey showed that people perceive a difference between forests and woods, especially those in higher socio-economic classes. The main differences are that forests are perceived as darker and denser, mainly conifer, man-made or cultivated. This shows that the word 'forest' has become associated with new plantation forests and that the connotations are somewhat negative. The forest landscape preferences are for those which blend into the landscape, have a lot of variety, are colourful and beautiful, look natural and have variably spaced trees. No strong like or dislike was shown for widely spaced trees, a forest as a defined feature in the landscape or for large-scale forests. Definite dislike was shown for trees planted in orderly rows. The visual preferences from the photographs were less informative than was hoped for but the results can be summarised as a preference for variety in the scene in terms of components (trees, water, open ground) and in terms of colours and the mix of trees. The least preferred scenes were the opposite: blank, dull, boring or uninteresting.

The findings of the Landscape Preference Study showed firstly, that the physical/aesthetic attributes rated by the landscape architects correlated quite well with the preferences shown by the public; moreover the suitability for different activities showed a significant pattern, with the scenes judged best for tourism, getting away, recreation, etc lying at the opposite end of the scale from that judged best for timber.

The research showed that members of the public are able to discriminate about landscapes from colour photographs and can make aesthetic and suitability judgements. These preferences accord quite well with the *a priori* judgements made by experienced professional landscape architects. It is to be expected that, as more designs following the forestry guideline principles are implemented, the public should be able to perceive an increase in landscape quality.

Scenic preference research often tends to reinforce the notion of landscape as separate from the observer, observed from a distance in a disinterested manner. It can result in landscape being treated as if it were a photograph or painting. This research attempted to avoid this by asking questions where observers had to imagine they had an interest in the landscape, and by using visitors to forests to make a more direct link between viewers and users. However, there remains the question of how well photographs represent the real world and our experience of it.

2. The Landscape Value of Farm Woodlands

Since 1988 the Government, through the Forestry Commission (FC) and Ministry of Agriculture, Fisheries and Food (MAFF), has paid farmers in England to take land out of agriculture and plant it with trees to produce woodlands of benefit both to the farmers, to the environment and to the nation. By 1996 some 18 400 hectares of new woodland had been approved under the Farm Woodland and Farm Woodland Premium Schemes and considerable amounts of money had been spent in the initial planting grants (FC) and annual payments (MAFF).

One of the benefits expected to be realised by planting farm woodlands is enhancement of the landscape. Many agricultural scenes had experienced losses of hedges, trees and woods by their removal or from Dutch Elm Disease, so that increasing woodland cover is anticipated to restore something of these losses.

In order to qualify for grants to plant woodland, farmers and landowners have to satisfy Forestry Commission environmental guidance. The landscape design guidance applicable to farm woodlands is contained in the Lowland Landscape Design Guidelines, a document written by technical experts (though subject to wide consultation) and containing design principles which, if followed, are expected to produce attractive landscapes giving a positive benefit to society.

In 1996 research was undertaken by Entec UK Ltd on behalf of MAFF and the Forestry Commission (Entec, 1996) to test certain of the major assumptions behind the design recommendations contained in the Lowland Landscape Design Guidelines. The outcome of the research is intended to be used to help revise (where necessary) that advice so as to reflect more accurately public perceptions and preferences.

The approach to the research was centred around personal interviews with a representative cross-section of the public, use of visual imaging (using photomontage techniques) to show different design options based on a number of the design principles laid down in the Lowland Landscape Design Guidelines. Qualitative measurements were made of public perceptions and attitudes to rural English landscapes, to woodlands in these landscapes and to variables in the layout and design of woodland. Single questionnaires were used for individual members of the public, excluding anyone involved with agriculture, forestry or landscape design. The interviews took place in five locations and the questions relating to landscape and woodlands were designed around pictures of landscapes characteristic of the locality where sampling took place.

Information about the respondents was collected on the basis of those which are normally the most statistically significant factors: gender, age, socio-economic class and the level of use of woodlands by respondents (which normally influences the degree of interest or care shown in the subject).

The design principles being tested for their validity operate quite differently depending on the character of the landscape, in particular the type or strength of landform and field patterns. Thus four generic and one 'special' landscape type were used so as to test the principles across their range of application, being flat ground, undulating topography, rounded landform, scarp and dip slopes and river valleys.

Sampling took place in five regions selected as being within or near one of the five landscape types. In each area two locations for interview were selected: a rural and an urban area. Interviews were conducted in the street during daylight hours in good weather so that as much time could be devoted as each respondent was willing to give.

The variables to be tested were the age at which trees are perceived to be a wood; preferences for different species mixtures; the optimum proportions for tree cover in the landscape; preferences for different woodland shapes and edge structures; the importance of screening eyesores; the preferred woodland character along paths; the impact of protection methods and felling. This was a long list of variables so individual respondents were only shown six or seven of them.

The variables (except for the age and internal views) were demonstrated using photomontage techniques. For each variable in each location a single photograph was adjusted using computer software (Adobe Photoshop) so that only the variable under test was different in each option. Respondents were asked to rate the most preferred and least preferred option for each variable and to explain why. The preferences were then analysed against the characteristics of the respondents, enabling patterns of preference to be linked to gender, age, socio-economic class and so on.

The results are summarized as follows. The age at which groups of trees are perceived by people to be a wood was when they were well grown and mature, especially in flat landscapes where the edge of a wood is the main external feature. This suggests associations with age and being able to walk beneath the trees.

The images used were all of conifers, so using broadleaved trees might have produced different results. However, if this finding is statistically significant, it will be some decades before recently planted woodlands will provide significant landscape benefits.

Species mix looked at preferences for the proportion between conifers and broadleaves. Preferences for pure broadleaves were strong and bore out the results from previous research. Of those who chose mixed woodland, however, the preference for mixtures of 70% conifer to 30% broadleaves was marginally higher while the mainly conifer option was the least liked image. Thus the preference for pure broadleaves as "more natural" is significant.

The scale of woodlands in a landscape relative to non-wooded areas is a key principle of design and in the guidelines the guiding rule of 2:1 or 1:2 ratio is given. There was a significant preference expressed for scenes showing two-thirds wooded while the least wooded option was least preferred.

Woodland shape was tested using designs of linear, rectangular, rounded and irregular shapes. There was a significantly greater preference for the irregular (organic) shape option, especially amongst frequent woodland users. This bears out the *a priori* principle that non-geometric shapes fitting into the landscape will be found more attractive by the public.

The woodland edge where it abuts fields is an important aspect of lowland landscapes. The *a priori* expectation is that varied, graded and diverse edges will be preferred over hard, abrupt ones or layered effects. Although the results were affected by the presence in each image of a rather obvious fence, the more natural and varied edge structure was preferred, matching the recommendations given in the guidelines.

Although not discussed in the guidelines, woodland is frequently cited as being good for screening unsightly objects such as busy roads or factories. Designers have often considered that integrating such features into the landscape may be better than full screening. The results of testing three options for screening a factory and two for a road showed a marked preference for complete screening, although the screening woodland should look natural.

The guidelines recommend variation in path alignment, spatial qualities and edge structure as being more attractive than straight, open paths. Is this true? The results showed a lot of variation but in general, the preference was for paths which were more enclosed and secluded, had sunlight coming through creating dappled shade and with more natural edges. The least preferred image was the straight, open example, which was considered unnatural, lacking variety and looked boring. This bears out the guideline recommendations.

Examples of straight, curved and varied alignment of rows of mixed conifers and broadleaves were shown to respondents, many of whom did not find any of the examples attractive. Most disliked the parallel straight lines. However, the image which was preferred overall by a very small margin was the option which most resembled the recommended layout given in the guidelines, that of blocks of differently aligned rows.

It takes a number of years for trees to become established so that the sight of fences or tree shelters is now a common one in the countryside. Three options were shown: a deer fence, white tree shelters and olive green tree shelters. The olive green shelters were significantly preferred. The fence was generally disliked while the white shelters were also unfavourably received. This bears out the guideline recommendations quite strongly.

Three options for felling were shown, although with hindsight their design would not have met the guideline standard. Large regular, large irregular and small irregular felling areas were tested. The smaller scale irregular blocks were preferred, seen as doing less damage to the view, while the large regular option was least preferred. This is in line with the recommendations in the guideline.

The overall conclusions to the research project showed that woodland is perceived as an integral part of the lowland English landscape and not as a separate component of it. Thus it is important for designers to consider woodland within the wider landscape context. The consistent theme running through the preferences was for naturalness and blending into the landscape, the landform and the existing woodland patterns. Variety is also valued. Conversely, people generally disliked unnatural, man-made, boring elements such as geometric shapes, straight paths, fences, and white tree shelters. On the whole, the principles contained in the Lowland Landscape Design Guideline which were tested, were broadly supported. Recommendations on woodland shape, scale, edge treatment, path layout, species mixes, felling coupes and tree shelters, presented as *a priori* assumptions of preference were all significantly reflected in the expressed preferences.

This research tried to test too much and suffered from images whose differences were too subtle for many people to appreciate. It also separated people from landscapes, although because of what was tested, that is specific design principles and not attitudes or basic preferences, this approach is valid. Valuable lessons can be learnt for future research. More testing of other design principles should be carried out to complete the start achieved here, so that the right balance can be struck between the views of professional and non-professional people.

3. Understanding People's Perceptions of Urban Fringe Woodlands

This research, carried out by Jacqueline Burgess of University College London (Countryside Commission, 1995) used in-depth interview techniques which took place out in woods in order to elicit people's feelings of safety when visiting wooded areas in the urban fringe. The research was commissioned by the Countryside Commission in connection with the Community Forest Initiative. Since one of the aims of community forests is to create attractive woodland landscapes close by people's homes it is important to know something of the factors that influence how much people are likely to visit them and gain enjoyment. There has been anecdotal evidence that many people are actually fearful of visiting woods and 'wild places', preventing them from visiting or gaining a full and enjoyable experience.

The project therefore aimed to explore whether different social and cultural groups felt that there were risks in visiting woods in urban fringe areas and if so what they were, to discover how much fear might prevent them from visiting and to recommend ways of reducing fears and of increasing use.

The researchers took thirteen groups, all of single gender but representing different age and cultural backgrounds, on guided walks through woodland in urban fringe areas followed by a discussion of their experiences. Some people were regular visitors to woods whilst others had never visited a woodland before. The groups were taken through dense areas, open spaces and followed different sorts of paths. The woods, outside London and near Nottingham, were all ancient woods of mixed character with some open canopies and former coppice areas. They were not recent plantations nor were they old hunting forests.

The focused discussion covered the pleasures of visiting woods; the causes and the effects of anxiety; specific aspects of woodland character and structure and how changes to management or design could reduce anxiety; crime and safety in woods compared with built up areas and how to meet different users' requirements.

From the discussion (which cannot be extrapolated as representative of the whole population) some key findings emerged. Firstly, the effect of enclosure, a key property that helps to define woodland, was significant. Enclosure could lead to perceptions of vulnerability to being trapped, of providing places where potential attackers could hide or where being out of sight of other people causes anxiety about being vulnerable or lost. Equally, it is the sense of enclosure that gives many of the positive qualities to woodland and makes people want to explore them. The degree and character of the way enclosure occurs are clearly important.

Secondly, women fear being in woodlands on their own. Some would need to be in pairs while others, especially Asian or Afro-Caribbean women, needed larger groups; although they wanted to explore and enjoy the 'wildness', anxiety over their personal safety overrode their capacity to enjoy their experience.

Thirdly, men do not feel the risk of being attacked to the same degree as women, but they are anxious about getting lost or trespassing. They were worried about the safety of their wives or daughters and all young children in terms of sexually-motivated crimes. They recognised that if they met a woman on her own in woods, they could be seen as threatening and this affected their behaviour.

The fears perceived by all participants were reinforced or increased by the media attention given to sex crimes, which is out of all proportion to their occurrence in general and in woodlands or parks in particular. Hence people tend to feel much more anxious or fearful than they need be.

Some of the research findings relate directly to the design of the woodland, of facilities and of information provided for visitors. Other findings for resolution depend on perceptions affected by other factors, such as the media. Several outcomes of the research relate to giving people a choice of woodland type and level of facilities so that some visitors can feel safer in more open, highly managed and 'policed' areas with lots of information whereas at the other extreme wilder areas with fewer facilities cater for those confident enough to want to be by themselves and able to explore, map read, etc.

There is a risk with this type of research that the results might be different for other sample groups and they cannot be extrapolated to the population as a whole. Thus, it may be necessary to expand the research in scale and repeat it over time in order to track changing perceptions. Policies and management practices need to be based on valid research and the lack of statistical analysis possible for this type of research method is a severe drawback.

4. The Aesthetic Experience of being in Woodland

The research into fear and anxiety concentrated on ways of reducing negative feelings. It did not explore the positive aspects and what aesthetic experience is specifically available from forests or woods that makes them special. Cheryl Foster, an aesthetician and philosopher who completed a PhD on the 'Aesthetics of Environment' at the University of Edinburgh, carried out an experiment in woodland in New Jersey, USA (Foster, 1996 unpublished). She accompanied three urban people into the woods and observed how they reacted as the visit progressed.

They went from situations where their busy thoughts preoccupied them towards a gradual immersion in the ambience of the forest and a calming down of their thoughts into a more reflective state. Foster was able to chart the points at which the stimuli of the sights, sounds, smells and kinaesthetic reactions engaged the subjects in a complete aesthetic experience. The stimulation involved natural features and contrasted with the enforced bombardment of stimuli found in urban settings, which we are forced to respond to whether we want to or not. The full aesthetic engagement is important, where the rhythms of walking, of wind in the trees, of water bubbling in a brook and the spatial enclosure of the forest appear to play on our senses in a very positive way, helping us to feel calm, refreshed, physically and mentally rejuvenated. The long accepted benefits of natural environments and specifically woodland, can be seen to be true as a result of such research, despite the small number of studies and subjects involved. The point of this research was to demonstrate that the aesthetic engagement was almost an involuntary one, that the people did not go to the woods with a specific purpose in mind but nevertheless became absorbed, calmed, relaxed and refreshed by their immersion in a natural environment.

This research is really just the tentative start of what could prove to be a valuable area of study. However, the design of the research experiment needs to be much more rigorous. It may be difficult to perform statistical analysis for the same reasons as described for the research into fear and safety described earlier.

5. Valuing Landscape Improvements in British Forests

The objective of this research was to assess the value which the British public places on forests managed to provide an enhanced landscape, relative to those managed for purely commercial output. It was commissioned by the Forestry Commission and carried out by Entec UK Ltd during 1996 (Entec, 1997). The research contained five elements: a literature review, focus group discussions, pilot testing of survey instruments, the main survey, analysis, interpretation and reporting.

The literature review was used to guide the conduct of the subsequent stages of the project. Key elements of the search were previous examples of the application of contingent valuation (CV) and other valuation methodologies to elicit preferences for forest types. From this it was concluded that CV methodology remains the most satisfactory method of valuation currently available. Familiarity with particular landscape types is more important than cultural or evolutionary factors in determining preference for landscapes, and strengths of preference vary over the human life cycle and are influenced by socio-economic status. The type of use of forest landscapes also influences preferences. The psychological analysis of the quality of information processing by survey respondents can be improved by asking them to voice their thinking aloud. Photomontage techniques (as used in the landscape value of farm woods research) should be used as a substitute for real life images but good contrast between images is essential.

The focus groups were intended to provide qualitative information to help in the design of the questionnaire and photographic presentation of material that was to be used in the main data collection part of the research. They allowed the number of landscape and payment vehicle options to be narrowed down to those that could be sensibly tested. Eight focus groups were undertaken, structured to provide a cross-section of people of regions throughout Britain (urban/rural location, gender, age, socio-economic class and type and frequency of countryside use).

From the focus groups it was found that there are different attitudes between local users of forest landscapes and urban-based people. Participants found it difficult to concentrate on appearance alone and could not easily dissociate themselves from recreational or wildlife values. The use of more distant scenes helped to overcome this. Of the landscape variables tested, edge and degree of open space elicited weak responses compared with shape, type of felling or species mixture. Edge and open space were dropped from further consideration. Seasonal changes to the landscape affected preferences. Significant demographic variables affecting preference are socio-economic group, age/life stage and frequency of forest use; the presence of children in the interviewee's family appears to be an important influence on preferences. Participants found it difficult to understand the concept of a marginal cost being incurred for a change in the landscape, so clear explanation was important. The importance and power of the imagery and the need to exclude distracting elements, to use the same scale, consistent image quality and high contrast between variables was highlighted. Participants were more consistent in their dislike (always the more commercial option) than their likes.

It was decided to include a choice experiment (CE) as well as the CV. The CE method presents respondents with a series of pairs of alternative combinations of forest design characteristics illustrated by photographic images. The CV uses willingness to pay (WTP) for a change in attributes (forest characteristics) using a payment vehicle such as taxation. After piloting and adjusting the structure and format of the survey instrument, national taxation was chosen as the payment vehicle and images were enhanced to convey the changes they illustrated better.

The survey design used approximately one-third of respondents in the choice experiment and two-thirds in the contingent valuation. Different sets of images were used in the two surveys and the samples were further split so that no respondent was asked to study more than three different image sets. Variables examined were the shape of felling areas, felling method (complete, patch clear felling, selection felling) and species mixes in autumn, spring and winter.

The sample (both overall and within each main sub-sample) is considered representative of GB residents in regional distribution, age and gender though not socio-economic group. It was considered acceptable as a basis for assessing willingness to pay values.

In the choice experiment each respondent was asked to choose a preferred option for each of four pairs of forest description. Each description varied according to four characteristics of cost, felling type, shape or species mix. It was found that choices between forest pairs are significantly affected depending on whether the respondent is a forest-user or non-user, lives in a rural area, has children, had a rural childhood, or is male or female. Average willingness to pay per household per year for each preferred variable ranged between £11.36 and £13.90.

In the contingent valuation responses were elicited in a sequence in which a respondent's most preferred choice was valued first (WTP1) and so on. Consequently it can be argued that WTP1> WTP2> WTP3. People were asked to express a WTP for their 'ideal' forest although this cannot be taken as an absolute measure because individual concepts of what constitutes 'ideal' may vary.

Bids obtained can be protest bids ("can pay, won't pay"); genuine zeros ("can't pay" or "no value") or genuine bids ("can pay, will pay"). An adequate number of genuine bids was obtained with the number of protest bids being consistent with similar studies. Standard statistical tests on the WTP values suggest that the results are robust. It is also considered acceptable to sum data across forest design variables; this enables cross-tabulation between WTP and respondent characteristics to be made eg:

WTP for enhancement	£/household/year	
recreational user vs non-user	32.76	20.16
visitor in last year vs non-visitor	31.53	18.54

WTPs for individual characteristics can also be isolated, but need to be taken into account whether the bids were first, second or third in sequence.

It can be concluded from the results that the survey performed well and that the data stand up well to close scrutiny. The WTP values confirm a public preference for natural looking forests whose shapes are organic and not geometric, where felling type is mainly smaller patches or selective felling and where there is a colourful species mixture. One exception was a preference for evergreen landscapes in winter (possibly a 'Christmas Card' effect). WTP values ranged from £9.33 to £12.75 per household per year, quite similar to the CE results.

From both sets of results it appears that members of the British public are willing to pay between £29 and £38 per household per year (combined WTPs) to see enhancements in the appearance of British forests which result in their perception of an 'ideal' forest emerging. Smaller sums would be paid for individual components of the ideal forest's design. However, as currently structured, the data cannot be applied to specific forests.

Conclusions

There are several conclusions that can be drawn from the research discussed here. Firstly, woods are an important part of the British landscape but are not seen as separate from the landscape as a whole. Secondly, people are happy to see more woodlands as long as they blend into the landscape and appear natural. There is a general preference for broadleaves, particularly in the lowlands, but evergreen conifers are acceptable in mixture with other species. Thirdly, diversity is important in the landscape and open space is valuable in larger forests. Fourthly, the design principles developed for forest landscapes by professional experts stand up well in producing results that the public find attractive. Fifthly, woods produce both positive and negative reactions for visitors depending on their perception of them as safe places to visit. Once fears are overcome, woods have a unique capacity to produce a positive aesthetic response which engages all the senses. The calming effect induced by a prolonged visit to an attractive, safe woodland can be significant and offer psychological benefits. Sixthly, people are willing to pay considerable sums of money to ensure that forests are made more attractive.

These conclusions point to the future and suggest key ways in which forests and woods should be expanded in order to meet the aesthetic requirements of the public. Forests and woods which fail to meet guideline standards should be improved as soon as practically possible and new woodlands should be designed to become integral parts of the landscape. Naturalness and visual diversity are key requirements. Designing to respond to local landscape character is also important. Attention should be paid to the layout of the interior of woodlands so that they are both safe and attractive. Spending money on landscape improvements will be rewarded by significant public benefit (although there is little likelihood of new funds becoming available specifically for such work).

The research described here is drawn from the two emerging trends. The first is the statistical approach that measures scenic preferences or willingness to pay based on tightly worded questionnaires and sophisticated photomontage techniques. This is the more objective method, it can be related to trends in the population as a whole and is valid for national policy and guideline formulation. Against this type of method is the risk that it measures the lowest common denominator of perception and that people are asked to judge things for which they have little or no knowledge. The alternative view is that this type of approach is essentially democratic and reflects the true views as opposed to those of a few professionals or an elite. The survey design and methodologies have matured for this approach but they suffer from the drawback that while they measure expressed preferences there is no way of finding out why these are held or what processes produce them.

The second research approach is that of the non-statistical, subjective methods of discussion and direct observation of behaviour in the landscape. This can delve deeper to unearth some of the reasons that produce the perceptions measured in the first type of approach. This is important, because we need to know the psychological and philosophical underpinning to design principles, for example. What is needed in this type of research is better experimental design and ways in which objective measurements can be made at the same time that the subjective assessments are recorded. This might include taking measurements of pulse rates, pupil dilations or galvanic skin responses, all measures used in laboratory experiments and well correlated to express preferences for different scenes, for example. These measures are problematic away from the laboratory at the moment.

No doubt the next generation of research will draw on and learn from the strengths and shortcomings of the methods used in the examples described here. The research has so far proved useful and policy makers, designers and managers have better information now than ever before about the preferences, perceptions and values placed on woodlands by the public.

References

Countryside Commission 1995 *Growing in Confidence* CCP457 Countryside Commission, Cheltenham.

Entec (UK) Ltd 1996 *The Landscape Value of Farm Woodlands*: Unpublished report to MAFF/FC.

Entec (UK) Ltd 1997 *Valuing Landscape Improvements to British Forests*. Unpublished report to Forestry Commission.

Forestry Commission 1989 *Forest Landscape Design Guidelines*. Forestry Commission, Edinburgh.

Forestry Commission 1992 *Lowland Landscape Design Guidelines*. HMSO, London.

Foster, C. 1996 Unpublished paper on the Reflective Aesthetic presented to International Conference on the Aesthetics of the Forest, Punkaharju, Finland.

Gibson, J. J. 1979 *The Ecological Approach to Visual Perception*. Houghton Mifflin, Boston.

Lee, T. R. in press *Forests, Woods and People's Preferences*. Technical Paper 18 Forestry Commission, Edinburgh.

Chapter 11

Conclusion: Woodlands in Context

Robin A. Butlin

Introduction

The contributions to this book of essays on woodland in the landscape in the past, present and future have illustrated, largely within the geographical confines of the United Kingdom, the complexity of issues that are associated with the study of this important resource and aesthetic asset. They also demonstrate the necessity and values of different disciplinary and temporal perspectives. The geographical scales of the essays range from continental to national and local, and demonstrate the advantages of different degrees of focus on particular places and the attendant variations in processes of change, both natural and human-induced. Huntley's opening chapter sets the scene with a detailed scientific analysis of the post-glacial history of the British woodlands within a European context, providing a necessary and helpful context for the later chapters, and introducing one of the key themes of the book: the dynamism of woodland environments through time, as influenced both by natural change and by human agency.

Historical and ecological contexts and sources

The study of the development of forest and woodland complexes through time has long been a topic of focus for historical geographers and environmental historians, and one of the more interesting developments of recent years has been the increasing attempt to combine and match documentary with environmental history, both on global and more restricted scales. This matching of human and natural archives affords major possibilities for the advancement of our knowledge of human impact on environmental change, though each set and sub-set of evidence has to be evaluated and tested with great care, and in recognition that the time periods of written documentary evidence are, of course, limited   (Butlin, 1993; Butlin and Roberts, 1995).

Pioneer work on the reconstruction of woodlands and forests in past times from documentary evidence, based initially on the data for woodland contained in the

Domesday Survey of 1086, was carried out by H. C. Darby and his collaborators in the major project which involved the reconstruction of the geographies of Domesday England. The mapping of references to woodland, by statements of length, breadth and area, and by references to such features as pannage for swine, gives an approximate measure of woodland for those areas covered by the survey (Darby, 1971,1973,1977). Use of this data set, with modified interpretation from that of Darby, has been made by Jones (Chapter 5), Gledhill (Chapter 6), and others in this book. The combination of this and other types of documented evidence, such as monastic surveys and extents (Kaner, Chapter 7), Anglo-Saxon charters, place-names, maps (from the sixteenth century onwards), and more modern descriptions and treatises, including natural histories and topographies, with field and remotely sensed evidence, allows accurate portraits to be built up of the dynamics of woodland and forest change for many regions in past times (Rackham, 1980, 1986, 1990).

The evidence available for tracing the historical ecology of woodlands is of increasing interest to scholars, through, for example, the survival of evidence of such practices as coppicing and pollarding, discovered and recorded by historic and contemporary field survey, and also the variety and richness of surviving woodland plant species and associated vegetation types (Gulliver, 1995; Marren, 1990; Watkins, 1991). All these ecological historic evidence types can, for the historic period, be supplemented by a range of documentary evidence, as is shown in this volume, *inter alia* in the chapters (2, 4, and 8) by Fleming, Rackham, and Watkins and Lavers.

Most of the studies in this book have dealt with developments in Britain, though a number make brief reference to parallel studies elsewhere. The comparative study of woodland history and management is a theme which is worth developing, both for methodological and for comparative evaluative purposes, not least when concerned with the rates of temporal change in forest and woodland communities, and the potential applications and efficiency of the use of traditional methods of woodland management in contemporary environments, as evaluated by Kirby in Chapter 3, and in relation to the role of ancient deadwood, reviewed in Chapter 8 by Watkins and Lavers.

One of the early syntheses of woodland change at a large scale was Darby's study of the changing woodland of Europe, in which he asserted that "perhaps the greatest single factor in the evolution of the European landscapes has been the clearing of the wood that once clothed almost the entire continent" (Darby, 1956, p. 183). Drawing on a wide range of research literature, including his own collaborative Domesday Book studies, he sketched out a chronology of woodland clearance in Europe from classical times to the early twentieth century, paying particular attention to the Middle Ages (notably the German colonization east of the Elbe) and to regional variations in clearing. Later large-scale studies of the evolution of woodland and forest include Williams' studies of the historical geography of the historic rates of deforestation at a global scale, and of the forests of North America (Williams, 1989a, b), work on the impact of Spanish and subsequent settlement on the ecosystems of the Caribbean islands (Sauer, 1966; Watts, 1987, 1995), and on tropical forests more generally (Flenley, 1979). There are numerous studies of the processes of woodland and forest evolution at smaller scales, as exemplified by a number of contributions to this volume, including those dealing with Yorkshire.

The complex processes associated both with deforestation and afforestation in areas of European colonial expansion from the sixteenth to the early twentieth century have been increasingly well documented (Tucker, 1988; Grove, 1990, 1995a, b), and afford interesting bases for comparative study with the experiences of Britain and Europe, even though the ecological and climatic contexts are much more varied than those reported by the contributors to this book. The question of the markets and demands for timber and wood products, increasingly in the early modern and modern periods subject to global scales of interaction, is an important one, as also is the vital and linked longer-term question of regeneration of woods and forests for purposes of what has come to be known as sustainable development. Although throughout much of the long period of human agency on the earth the demand for and use of woodland and forest products has been local - its exact nature depending on its environmental and socio-economic and technical contexts of particular times - the requirements of increasingly specializing economies from the time of the early industrial revolution in Britain and Europe in particular led to re-orientations of demand. On the one hand the technology for the use of coal and steam-power led to a reduction in the demand for wood for smelting, and ultimately for the construction of ships, but on the other hand the new technologies themselves required timber in, for example, coalmines for use as pit-props and as sleepers on the rapidly developing railway systems.

The habits of consumption of the capitalist economies led to demand for hardwood timber and for the clearance of forest regions in the colonies for the development of commercial plantations, such as the European tea plantations of Assam and North Bengal, based on land purchased from the government of British India after 1833 (Tucker, 1988, 123). Rackham (Chapter 4) refers to the collapse of the shipbuilding and tanning markets in England in the 1860s as a result of the transport of fossil fuels, as a consequence of which woods fell into misuse, though there was in some areas delay in moving to continental European methods of forestry management and timber production. Jones (Chapter 5) has indicated similar developments in the extinction of traditional woodland management in the coal measure woodlands of South Yorkshire, with coppicing declining steadily in the nineteenth century as a result of the use of coal for smelting for lead and iron and of urban expansion. The expansion of the industrial economies of Britain and of the urban and industrial populations thus, it could be argued, was at one and the same time causing the decline of traditional woodland management methods, while facilitating the destruction of tropical hardwoods by demand for the hardwoods themselves and for the products of the plantations by which many forest areas were replaced.

This is, of course, a very simple concept: reality was much more complex. Britain, with its rapid and high density of population growth in industrial areas, was for quite some time exceptional, and the actual experience of other parts of Europe was quite different, partly depending on their ecological characteristics as well as their different histories of economic and social development. The environmental impact of industrialization was lower in Sweden, for example, even though there was a reduction in forest land at the expense of an increase in arable land during the period 1800-1860. In more modern times, the relatively recent factor of environmental pollution of forest and other areas of Scandinavia has partly been attributed to its own paper-producing industry, but also to such regionally shared factors as acid rain and to fall-out from atomic weapons-testing and nuclear accidents (Simmons, 1998). Woodland change in the eighteenth, nineteenth and twentieth centuries in Eastern Europe and European Russia was quite dramatic, influenced as much by social factors as the abolition of serfdom, increased populations and increased markets for the sale of timber as by industrialization directly (Simmons, 1998).

Images of woodland: representations, aesthetics and symbolism
While the historic evolution of areas of woodland and forest, as evidenced by palaeoecological evidence, documented accounts and survival of relic features which can be mapped, classified and analysed, is an important approach and set of perspectives, there are other ways of looking at woodland in the past, at the present, and in the future. These are less 'scientific' and more subjective, but of equal importance.

The images of woodland in literature is a topic not well reflected in the chapters in this book, but has a significant history. The role of woodland in fairy tales and pantomimes – *Little Red Riding Hood* and *Babes in the Wood,* for example – is a reflection of a frequently experienced natural environment used as a context for folktales with such familiar contents as insecurity, sense of loss and alienation, and threat from malicious people and from animals. Equally, moral tales of folk heroism can stem from such images: as in the case of Robin Hood, for example, associated with Sherwood Forest in the East Midlands, and described in a different, scientific, context in Chapter 8 of this book by Watkins and Lavers.

Literary and symbolic aspects of woodland and of trees, including their significance for national images, have an interesting literature. Thomas, in his *Man and the natural World* (1983), in the chapter on 'Trees and Flowers', narrates the deforestation of England from Mesolithic times onwards. Though claiming that although there may have been some exaggeration in contemporary accounts of the extent of deforestation in the sixteenth and seventeenth centuries, nonetheless there was substantial reduction in the number of trees in England at this time : "Disparking, enclosure of chases, encroachment on the commons, the lax administration of the local forests and the steady reduction in their extent: all meant the clearing of the woodland and the felling of trees. It was not on Tower Hill that the axe made its most important contribution to English history" (Thomas, 1983, 193).

Realization that the replacement of these lost assets was necessary led to initiation of new phases of tree planting in the early modern period, both in royal forests such as the Forest of Dean and the New Forest, and on private estates, the motivations being both economic and aesthetic, the latter becoming even more important in the enthusiasms for landscape gardening in the eighteenth century. Enthusiasm for the furnishing of the landscape with trees is expressed in a wide range of contemporary literature, one of the most well-known enthusiasts and experts being John Evelyn, whose discourse on tree-planting, *Sylva*, published in 1664, followed concerns at the shortage of timber for the construction of ships for the navy.

In the eighteenth and early nineteenth centuries, as Daniels has shown in his essay on the political iconography of woodland in later Georgian England (Daniels, 1988), there was a complex overlapping of a range of interests in the practicalities and symbolisms of woods and trees. The practical advantages of trees planted to improve scenery and economic returns on estates, together with the important national symbolism of the oak tree, contrasted with the associations of forest customary use practices with 'the continuing association with lawlessness', (Daniels, 1988, 44; Daniels and Seymour, 1990), whose control was effected by law, some of it quite draconian. Patrician associations of parkland planted trees were strongest through oak trees, which "were claimed to be venerable, patriarchal, stately, guardian and quintessentially English" (Daniels, 1988, 48), though other trees with patrician associations included the elm and conifers.

Such related themes of aesthetic qualities, security and taste are also examined, in the contemporary and projected future contexts, in the chapters in this book by S. Bell (Chapter 10) and Bell and Child (Chapter 9), in relation to the analysis of public perception of woodlands in the landscape, their use for recreational, therapeutic, economic, and scientific ends, and the local, regional and national symbolism that they signify. Of particular help to an understanding of the wide potential role of woodland in a modern society is Bell and Child's analysis of the National Forest (Chapter 9), with its significant points of focus on the basic needs for environmental protection and enhancement, for the sustenance of multiple roles and functions of forests and woodlands, for the application of science to the planting process and a public understanding of 'green' science, for the understanding of the inclusive nature of this process and for a recognition of the moral message of forest and woodland development. These are all key themes, together with the clear recognition, in all the contributions to this book, of the complexity and dynamics of forest and woodland evolution and change throughout prehistoric and historic time, and thus for the understanding of this important landscape feature and process of environmental understanding and management for the next century and beyond.

References

Butlin, R.A., 1993, *Historical Geography. Through the Gates of Space and Time*, Edward Arnold, London.

Butlin, R.A. and Roberts, N. (eds), 1995, *Ecological Relations in Historical Times*. Blackwell, Oxford.

Daniels, S., 1998, The political iconography of woodland in later Georgian England, in Cosgrove, D. and Daniels, S. (eds), *The Iconography of Landscape,* Cambridge University Press, Cambridge.

Daniels, S. and Seymour, S., 1995, Landscape design and the Idea of Improvement 1730-1914, in Dodgshon, R.A. and Butlin, R.A. (eds), *An Historical Geography of England and Wales*, Second Edition, Academic Press, London, pp. 487-520.

Darby, H.C., 1956, The clearing of the woodland in Europe, in Thomas, W.L. Jr (ed.), *Man's role in changing the face of the Earth,* Chicago University Press, Chicago, pp.183-216.

Darby, H.C., 1971, *The Domesday Geography of Eastern England*, Cambridge University Press, Cambridge.

Darby, H.C. 1973, Domesday England, in Darby, H.C. (ed.), *A New Historical Geography of England,* Cambridge University Press, Cambridge, pp.39-74

Darby, H.C., 1977, *Domesday England*, Cambridge University Press, Cambridge.

Flenley, J., 1979, *The equatorial rainforest: a geological history*, Butterworth, London.

Grove, R.H., 1990, Colonial conservation, ecological hegemony and popular resistance: towards a global synthesis, in MacKenzie, J. (ed.), *Imperialism and the Natural World*, Manchester University Press, Manchester, pp.14-50.

Grove, R.H., 1995a, *Green Imperialism. Colonial expansion, tropical island Edens and the origins of environmentalism 1600-1860*, Cambridge University Press, Cambridge.

Grove, R. H., 1995b, Imperialism and the discourse of desiccation: the institutionalization of global environmental concerns and the role of the Royal Geographical Society, 1860-1880, In Bell, M., Butlin, R.A., and Heffernan M.J. (eds), *Geography and Imperialism 1820-1940*, pp.36-52.

Gulliver, R., 1995, Woodland history and plant indicator species in north-east

Yorkshire, England, in Butlin, R.A. and Roberts, N. (eds), *Ecological Relations in Historical Times*, Blackwell, Oxford, pp.169-190.

Marren, P., 1990, *Woodland Heritage*, David and Charles, Newton Abbot.

Rackham, O., 1980, *Ancient Woodland*, Edward Arnold, London.

Rackham, O., 1986, *The History of the Countryside*, Dent, London.

Rackham, O., 1990, *Trees and Woodland in the British Landscape*, Second Edition, Dent, London.

Sauer, C. O., 1966, *The Early Spanish Main*, Berkeley and Los Angeles, University of California Press.

Simmons, I.G., 1998, Towards an environmental history of Europe, in Butlin, R.A. and Dodgshon, R.A. (eds), *An Historical Geography of Europe*, Oxford University Press, Oxford, pp.335-361.

Thomas, K., 1983, *Man and the Natural World. Changing attitudes in England, 1500-1800*, Allen Lane, London.

Tucker, R.P., 1988, The depletion of India's forests under British Imperialism: planters, foresters, and peasants in Assam and Kerala, in Worster, D. (ed.), *The ends of the Earth. Perspectives on modern environmental history*, Cambridge University Press, Cambridge, pp.118-140.

Watkins, C., 1991, *Woodland Management and Conservation*, David and Charles, Newton Abbot.

Watts, D., 1987, *The West Indies: patterns of Development, Culture and Environmental Change since 1492*, Cambridge University Press, Cambridge.

Watts, D., 1995, Ecological responses to ecosystem shock in the Island Caribbean: the aftermath of Columbus, 1492-1992, in Butlin, R.A. and Roberts, N.(eds), *Ecological Relations in Historical Times*, Blackwell, Oxford, pp. 267- 279.

Williams, M., 1989a, Deforestation: past and present, *Progress in Human Geography*, 13, pp.176-207.

Williams, M., 1989b, *Americans and their forests. A historical geography*, Cambridge University Press, Cambridge.

Appendix: Poster Presentations

Indicators and Invaders: the Status of Some Target Woodland Plants in Yorkshire

Stephen Hartley and Michel Ribodeau

Introduction and Methods

A rapid assessment of woodland flora was made at sixty-seven plots distributed across fifty-five woodlands in North and West Yorkshire (see Fig. 1). The study area can be broadly divided into three regions: 1) lower Wharfedale, which is a rolling landscape of mixed farming with an underlying geology of Millstone Grit. 2) A band of Magnesian Limestone which runs north-south to the east of Leeds, this is the most heavily wooded section in the study area. 3) The Vale of York, an intensively farmed plain of sandstone and alluvial deposits.

The survey method was similar to that described in the National Vegetation Classification handbook for woodland habitats (Rodwell 1991). Ground and field flora were recorded from a 20x20m plot, whilst the plot was extended to 50x50m for understorey and canopy species. Abundances of vascular plant species were scored on a five point scale of percentage cover: 1) 0.1-2%, 2) 3-10%, 3) 11-25%, 4) 26-50%, 5) 51-100%.

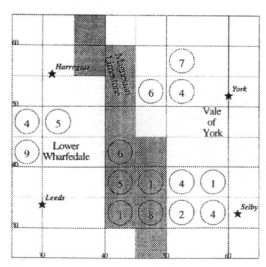

Figure 1 Location of study sites, numbers inside circles indicate the number of sites per 5km national square

Results

Half of the sites were located in semi-natural broadleaf woodland, one-quarter were mixed, 16% were

Indicators and Invaders: the Status of Some Target Woodland Plants in Yorkshire

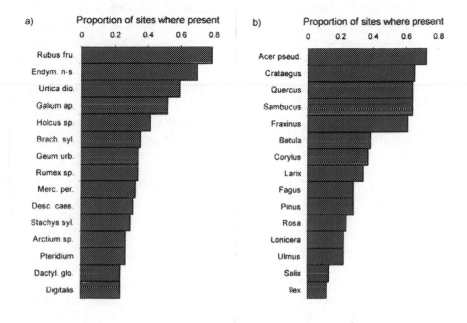

Figure 2 The fifteen most frequent species in (a) ground and field layer and (b) canopy and understorey

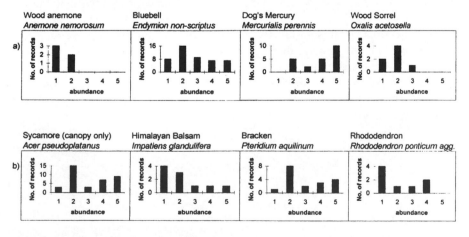

Figure 3 Abundances of (a) four ancient woodland indicators and (b) four 'invasive, species at the sites where they are present. Note the changing scale of the y-axis.

conifer plantation, 7% broadleaf plantation and just two sites (3%) were broadleaf coppice, which is probably a fair representation of the proportions of the different woodland types across the region. Fig. 2a and 2b illustrate the fifteen herbaceous and woody species that were most consistently present within the woodland plots. Bramble (*Rubus fruticosus* agg.) was the most frequent component of the ground flora, often at greater than 50% cover. Bluebells (*Endymion non-scriptus*) were the second most frequent plant, although only occasionally did they form dense carpets (see Fig. 3a). Sycamore (*Acer pseudoplatanus*) was the most frequent tree species, followed closely by Ash (*Fraxinus excelsior*) and Oak (*Quercus* sp.). In the understorey, Hawthorn (*Crataegus monogyna*) and Elder (*Sambucus nigra*) were the most frequent shrubs.

Not surprisingly, plant species are not evenly distributed across the region. Table 1 illustrates those species that are significantly over- or under-represented in the three different areas. The most striking pattern is shown by Dog's Mercury (*Mercurialis perennis*). Of its twenty-two occurrences, seventeen are on the Magnesian Limestone, four in lower Wharfedale and only one in the Vale of York. This observation is in accordance with Grime *et al.* (1988) who note that Dog's Mercury is 'particularly abundant in limestone woodlands'. Conversely, Bluebells were under-represented on the limestone, probably due to their requirement for deeper, moister soils (Grime *et al.*, 1988). There are only ten records of Himalayan Balsam (*Impatiens glandulifera*) so it is difficult to draw firm conclusions about its distribution, however the indications are that it is more widespread in the Vale of York.

Fig. 3a shows the abundances of four species that have been shown to be reasonable indicators of ancient woodland in Lincolnshire (Peterken, 1991), whilst Fig. 3b shows four species that have been considered as invasive. Himalayan Balsam is particularly interesting as it is normally associated with riparian habitats, but as the current results show, it is also capable of invading and dominating moist, open woodlands. At present, there is little data on how quickly it may come to dominate a woodland, although at Askham Bog (a wooded fen near York) it has achieved an average rate of radial spread of 6 m yr^{-1} since first being recorded in 1974 (Perrins, Fitter & Williamson 1993). This is one species whose status should be monitored over the coming years.

	Lower Wharfedale	Magnesian Limestone	Vale of York
Significantly more occurrences than expected by chance	*Larix** (*Digitalis pur.***)	*Mercurialis per.**** *Arctium* sp.* *Geum urbanum**	*Lonicera peri.*** (*Impatiens glan.***)
Significantly less occurrences than expected by chance	*Geum urbanum*** *Brachypodium syl.**	*Digitalis pur.*** *Endymion n-s.** *Holcus* spp.* (*Impatiens glan.**)	*Mercurialis per.****

Table 1. *** p < 0.001, ** p < 0.01, * p < 0.05. Chi-squared tests were carried out separately for the number of occurrences in each area against an aggregated value for the other two areas. Species in brackets had small sample sizes and therefore expected values less than five (but greater than three); the significance of these results must be accepted with caution.

Conclusion

The data presented here provide a regional snapshot of the frequency and abundance of various woodland plant species that are of interest to conservationists. The results characterise our present-day woodlands and landscapes. If a similar survey could be undertaken in future years it might be possible to assess how the florisitic face of our woodlands is changing.

Acknowledgements

We should like to thank all the land owners and farmers who granted us access to their land. We also thank Maxine Curzon who assisted on one of the surveys and Phyl Abbott who provided botanical advice.

References

Grime, J.P., Hodgson, J.G. & Hunt, R. 1988 *Comparative Plant Ecology: A Functional Approach to Common British Species*, Unwin Hyman, London.

Perrins, J., Fitter, A. & Williamson, M. 1993 Population biology and rates of invasion of three introduced *Impatiens* species in the British Isles. *Journal of Biogeography*, **20**, 33-44.

Peterken, G.F. 1981 *Woodland Conservation and Management*, Chapman and Hall, London.

Rodwell, J.S. 1991 *British Plant Communities: Volume 1, Woodlands and Scrub*, Cambridge University Press, Cambridge.

Strategies for Resolving Problems of Management of Urban-fringe Woodlands

Possible approaches to these issues were outlined in Rotherham (1991), Rose and Rotherham (in press) and Jones (1993), with novel ways of managing urban woods described in Jones and Talbot (1995). Taking the Sheffield case-study, critical issues have been addressed in the Sheffield Nature Conservation Strategy (1991), the Sheffield Woodland Policy (1987), and the South Yorkshire Forest Plan (1994). The latter initiative is a major stimulus for innovative approaches to resolving long-standing, and increasingly urgent problems. Pump-priming funding through the South Yorkshire Forest Programme has proved invaluable.

Examination of sites throughout Sheffield area shows that the type of management imposed on a wood varies tremendously. Size, location and ownership are important, and general trends can be recognised. These were described in terms of zones of open space management by Rotherham (1994) with a range of zones recognised in and around urban areas. In practice these represent points along a continuum as shown in Table 1.

Table 1 Zones of Open Space in Urban Areas (from Rotherham, 1994)

i.	Working or Rural Countryside:	rural woodland, moorland, farmland.
ii.	Countryside Fringe:	abandoned 'Working Countryside', river corridors, woodlands, golf courses.
iii.	Urban Countryside or Urban river 'Wildspace':	urban woodlands, less formal parks, urban corridors, disused allotments, golf courses, 'urban commons', other 'green corridors'.
iv.	Formal Open Space:	formal parks, gardens and landscape areas, allotment gardens, sports fields.
v.	The Built Environment:	

There is increasing urbanisation from (i) to (v) and increasing rural character from (v) to (i).

Working or Rural Countryside

This is generally land outside the built environment, managed as an integral part of the local economy, with large areas in both private and public ownership, and varying degrees of access and recreational use. It may have major social, economic and conservation value.

Countryside Fringe and Urban Countryside

These include land either within or beyond the boundary of the urban area, usually maintained for recreation or conservation use, or effectively abandoned. Due to its close proximity to major centres of human population, it is often under severe pressure. It may still have high conservation and recreation interest. River corridors often run through the urban heartland, providing links and corridors for wildlife movement and colonisation. Substantial relict woodlands, grasslands and even heaths may occur as units within urban areas.

Relict Landscapes

This is abandoned countryside now locked in urban areas, with unique wildlife and social value. They are often 'time capsules' of former landscapes and land-use. There are problems of isolation, although this may be more cosmetic than real. Many wildlife species may 'hop' from one 'habitat-node' to another.

The protection and conservation of these sites in a strategic context, buffered, and perhaps linked by green corridors, secondary spontaneous and created environments, must be a key long-term goal. In urban and rural-fringe areas we are not dealing with untouched, primary landscapes, rather they are human-influenced areas of tremendous local character. There is a need to recognise this context in terms of pragmatic approaches to safeguard the unique character, and yet allow for inevitable and ecologically-interesting changes. Location in heavily populated areas presents problems, but also provides a unique opportunity for local community involvement in conservation. These areas give urban communities access to, and an insight into, the unique conservation value of our historic landscapes. These are far more relevant to them than our most precious nature conservation sites out in the rural area.

Urban and urban-fringe woodlands are a very integral part of these broad landscape-types and their long-term management must be considered in this context. The importance of a co-ordinated strategic approach, and in particular, the involvement of the local community, was emphasised by Rotherham (1991 and 1994). The vital role of local authorities and statutory agencies in facilitating this involvement cannot be too highly stressed.

Conclusions

Ancient woods, especially in urban and urban-fringe locations clearly present their managers with a unique suite of problems. The cessation of traditional 'woodland' management and often the imposition of 'high forest' practice, have led to serious declines in ground flora and tree quality, and associated erosion of soils. Lack of awareness of the need for management, or of the particular sensitivity of historic woodland sites generates further difficulties. These exacerbate the sensitivity of neglect, abandonment and decline.

Whilst woodlands in urban areas may present acute difficulties, they also present enormous opportunities, often preserving a unique palimpsest of local history and archaeology which links closely to their present day, ecological interest - woods can be centres for community interest and opportunity. Management should not seek to preserve woods as fossilised examples of the past, but should recognise their dynamic nature, in the context of their unique history and former management. The re-introduction of small-scale, or at least moderate areas of managed coppice, linking to the production of charcoal and other traditional woodland craft products, can be the catalyst for community involvement. This may generate the *process* for managing ancient woodlands sustainably in the future. To achieve this successfully we must understand the relevance of landscape history to our vision of future management.

Acknowledgements

The authors wish to thank all those who have been involved in the conservation and management of Sheffield's woods, over many years. In particular, Mel Jones, Ted Talbot, Dan Lewis, William Fairhead, Jean Glasscock, Len Carr, Sal Pereira, Nick Burton, and all the active voluntary groups working for woods in our area. We also thank Valerie Staley and the Woodland Trust for their support at Owler Carr Woods, and both Paul Ardron and Chris Percy for assistance and fieldwork.

References

Anon. 1987 *Sheffield Woodland Strategy*, Sheffield City Council, Sheffield.

Anon. 1994 *South Yorkshire Forest Plan*, South Yorkshire Forest team, Sheffield.

Bannister, N. R., 1996 *Woodland Archaeology in Surrey: Its Recognition and Management*, Surrey County Planning Department, Kingston-upon-Thames.

Beswick, P. and Rotherham, I. D. (eds.), 1993 *Ancient Woodlands: Their Archaeology And Ecology:* National Conference Proceedings 25-26 April 1992, Landscape Conservation Forum, 1993.

Bownes, J. S., Riley, T., Rotherham, I. D. and Vincent, S. M., 1991 *Sheffield Nature Conservation Strategy*, Sheffield City Council, Sheffield.

Jones, M. 1993 *Sheffield's Woodland Heritage*, Second Edition, Green Tree Publications, Rotherham.

Jones, M. Talbot, E., 1995 Coppicing in urban woodlands - a progress report on a multi-purpose feasibility study in the City of Sheffield, *Journal of Practical Ecology and Conservation*, **1**, (1), 48-54.

Rackham, O., 1986 *The History of the Countryside*, J. M. Dent and Sons Ltd., London.

Rackham, O., 1989 *The Last Forest*, J. M. Dent and Sons Ltd., London.

Rose, J. C. and Rotherham, I. D., 1991 Problems of Conserving Urban Wildlife with Reference to Site Management, Translocation and Creation within Sheffield, United Kingdom: *Proceedings of BES Conference on Habitat Creation and Wildlife Conservation in Urban and Post-Industrial Environments*, Nottingham, 1991, in press.

Rotherham, I. D., 1994 The role of local authorities in conserving biodiversity through environmental management and land-use planning: *Proceedings of the VIth International Congress of Ecology*, Manchester, 1994, 77.

Rotherham, I. D., 1994, Conserving wildlife in urban relict countryside, Bulletin, *Yorkshire Naturalists' Union*, Bulletin, **22**, 2-4.

Rotherham, I. D., 1996, The sustainable management of urban-fringe woodland for amenity and conservation objectives, *Aspects of Applied Biology*, **46**, 33-38.

Rotherham, I. D., 1996, Woods in the heart of a city, *Yorkshire Wildlife*, Autumn 1996, 10-12.

Rotherham, I. D. and Ardron, P. A., 1996, A preliminary account of charcoal and whitecoal sites in woodlands around Sheffield and the eastern Peak District, *Peak District Journal of Natural History and Archaeology*, in press.

Rotherham, I. D. and Doram, G. P., 1990, A Preliminary Study of the Vegetation of Ecclesall Woods in Relation to Former Management, *Sorby Record*, **27**, 60-70.

Rotherham, I. D. and Jones, M. (eds.), 1997 The Natural History of Ecclesall Wood, *Part 1*, *A Special Publication of the Peak District Journal of Natural History and Archaeology*, Wildtrack Publishing, Sheffield.

The York Archaeological Wood Centre

Jim Spriggs and Ian Panter

Organic remains, and principally wood, are regularly found preserved in waterlogged deposits owing to the exclusion of oxygen. Naturally-occurring wetlands, elevated water tables in ancient urban centres, marine and estuarine environments annually produce finds of wood dating from remote prehistory onwards. Run jointly by English Heritage and the York Archaeological Trust, the York Archaeological Wood Centre (YAWC) was formed in 1993 to record, research and conserve wood remains (and other materials) from all these environments.

The Evidence

Whatever its provenance, the study of ancient worked wood provides a unique insight into human exploitation of this most precious resource. Careful examination of objects, structures and assemblages of wood provides evidence for past practices in the selection of wood for specific purposes: woodland management and land clearance; use and re-use of timber; and methods of working in wood (the 'toolkit'). Wood is examined to determine species, growth rate (rings per cm.) and other data that will shed light on the wood stock from which the 'find' derived. Samples may also be taken for dendrochronology, to provide a possible felling date, and to suggest in which part of the U.K. or (occasionally) foreign country the wood originated.

Preservation

Even though preserved over hundreds or thousands of years through waterlogging, wood will have become partially degraded through fungal and bacterial action, and through the gradual dissolution of the cellulose fraction of the wood make-up. Preservation techniques employed at the YAWC seek to replace the wood substance lost while removing most of the water that fills the fragile wood structure. After the application of a range of non-destructive techniques to survey the condition of the wood, it is immersed in tanks of a water-soluble polymer, polyethylene glycol, and the concentration gradually raised until the calculated content is achieved. The remaining water is then removed by accelerated freeze-drying in one of three freeze-drier units housed at the YAWC.

Projects
Practical work stems from finds of archaeological wood from both land-based and marine environments in the U.K. and further afield. Two major boat finds from the Severn Estuary, the Barlands Farm Romano-Celtic boat (Newport Museum) and the Magor Pill medieval boat (National Museums and Galleries of Wales), are both at the YAWC at present, undergoing pre-treatment. Marine material from the Elizabethan wreck being investigated off the coast of Alderney is also being researched and conserved at the YAWC, and a consultancy in Malaysia to advise on the conservation of a Dutch East Indiaman is also under way. Students of conservation receive training and work experience at the YAWC, and interested groups are always welcome to visit to see current projects in progress.

The Future
The YAWC facilities are continually being improved and enlarged as the value and information potential of archaeological waterlogged wood is increasingly appreciated. As the demand for our services grows, the York Archaeological Wood Centre is fast becoming recognised as a major national facility for the research and conservation of waterlogged archaeological and heritage material.

Illustrating Distribution Patterns of Hedgerow Classes and Broad-Leaved Woodlands in the Planned and Ancient Landscapes of Hampshire, Using GIS

Monty Loftus, Christine Butler,
Geordie McMillan and Alan Boyle

Recent work by the company BKS Surveys Ltd. has provided what may be the most complete digital data set of its kind on woodlands, hedges and other habitats and land uses throughout the whole of an English lowland county. To demonstrate the power of the analysis, two samples of landscape were selected from the 4000 sq. km. of digital mapping available. These samples, each of 25 sq. km., are known to exemplify distinctive ancient and planned (enclosure) landscapes, centred respectively on the parish of Rotherwick (ancient) at SU75NW and on Crawley (planned) at SU43SW.

The analysis done for Hampshire County Council was based on newly flown 1:20,000 air photos in colour, on which hedgerows and lines of trees were classified into six groups based on their height, width and whether or not planted. Woods were classified to English Nature Phase 1 mapping criteria, slightly amended. The poster displayed showed full colour printouts of the scanned colour imagery together with separate maps showing woods and hedges. Detailed analyses were presented.

The analysis that yielded these data was performed on flight lines of overlapping air photos viewed stereoscopically at 5x magnification. These were also scanned (to give a digital image) and rectified using *ERDAS Imagine* to occupy correct geographical space and accord with the map coordinates. All the land use area (polygons) and hedgerows were then entered digitally over the corrected scanned image to form two data layers, which can be manipulated separately and in any combination of elements within the geographic information system (GIS) software ARC INFO. The value of this interpretation and the accompanying technical procedures is that any part of the county can be displayed for any element, its area, length and number of occurrences and data can be extracted instantly using the software. Maps of single or combinations of land use elements may be printed to bring out patterns which may elude visual analysis.

Hedgerows

The 25 sq. km. of landscape around Crawley contains over 105 km. of hedgerow split into five classes. The Rotherwick sample has 144 km. in six classes. Rotherwick has a larger proportion of taller and wider hedges than Crawley. The most significant difference is that Rotherwick (ancient) has 62 km. of treed hedgerow as compared to 30 km. in Crawley. Its 6.5 km. of trees along streams and rivers reflects the fundamental difference in landscape (Tertiary loams versus chalk with no surface drainage). Planted tree lines and avenues were also more extensive in Rotherwick. All of this has implications for the origins of the landscape, its maintenance, its habitats and movement of species, as well as in landscape terms to the sense of enclosedness that an observer experiences in each.

Woodlands

Woodlands in Crawley amount to 172 hectares in 70 parcels. In Rotherwick there are 173 woods totalling 366 hectares. They have a smaller mean area and a higher standard deviation than those around Crawley, indicating that they are more widely dispersed. Though this might easily be read from map or photo, the analysis allows precise and immediate comparisons to be made.

GIS combined with photo interpretation is therefore shown as an effective tool in illustrating large-scale distribution patterns of interest to historians and landscape ecologists. The methodology used in this project involved over eighty land use categories, which described urban residential and non-residential, non-urban built areas, quarries and waste disposal land, agricultural and semi-natural habitats. The Council plan to use this mapping to assist them in planning and policy decisions across a range of management issues.

FARMING AND WILDLIFE ADVISORY GROUP
WOODLAND ADVICE

The Farming and Wildlife Advisory Group (FWAG) is an independent organisation with charitable status which aims to help farmers and landowners to improve the integration of wildlife and landscape conservation with their farming operations, and encourage environmentally responsible farming.

FWAG has County-based Farm Conservation Advisers who can prepare *Landwise* reports and plans, including advice on woodlands. The FWAG advisory service includes:

- A free initial advisory visit to farmers and landowners.
- Site assessment and design of new woodland planting schemes, including new native woodlands.
- Preparation of management plans for existing woodlands.
- Advice of grant sources and preparation of grant applications and bids.
- Costing of schemes and organising implementation and management.
- Design of related features including boundary hedges, ponds, rides and glades, and establishment of native ground flora.
- Woodland events and training courses, including woodland walks, charcoal making, hurdle making and new woodland creation.

For further information please contact your local FWAG Office.

North Yorkshire

Philip Lyth or Andrew Parkinson   ☎ *01609 783632 or*
Farm Conservation Advisers   *Fax 01609 774985*
FWAG in North Yorkshire
South Parade
NORTHALLERTON
North Yorkshire. DL7 8AQ

National

FWAG   ☎ *01203 696699*
National Agricultural Centre   *Fax: 01203 696760*
Stoneleigh
Kenilworth
WARWICKSHIRE
CV8 2RX

W.............. ....e:
Past and Future Perspectives

Edited by Margaret A. Atherden
and Robin A. Butlin

The PLACE Research Centre
University College of Ripon & York St John

Published by Leeds University Press

Cover photograph: Woodland in Caydale, North Yorkshire. Margaret Atherden

Printed by University Print Services
A division of Media Services at Leeds

ISBN   0 85316 186 0